Yesterday's Sports, Today's Math

by Don Fraser

Dale Seymour Publications®

Project Editor: Joan Gideon
Production Coordinator: Shannon Miller
Art: Susan Jaekel, Terry Guyer
Text and Cover Design: Nancy Benedict
Published by Dale Seymour Publications®, an imprint of the
Alternative Publishing Group of Addison-Wesley Publishing Company.

Order Number DS21492

ISBN 1-57232-200-4

2 3 4 5 6 7 8 9 10-VG-00 99 98 97 96

DALE
SEYMOUR
PUBLICATIONS®
P.O. BOX 10888
PALO ALTO, CA 94303

CONTENTS

SECTION 3   Basketball   33

SECTION 4   Hockey   55

INTRODUCTION

Do you have students in the fourth through ninth grade? Do any of them like sports? If so, then *Yesterday's Sports, Today's Math* (YSTM) is for you!

YSTM Is Up-to-Date

YSTM is always up-to-date. How can this be? Through a current newspaper among other sources, the students have an opportunity to work with the latest sports' results.

YSTM Encourages the Use of Local Statistics

Statistics from male professional leagues dominate the newspaper. However, students should be encouraged to provide statistics from college and from high school and from their own games and leagues. This way there can be a balance of statistics from men's and women's games and from professional and amateur sports.

YSTM Supports the Curriculum

YSTM provides the kind of learning emphasized in current curriculum standards. As students use YSTM, they not only get practice with computation using whole numbers, fractions, and percents, but they are using those skills to explore numbers from real life. They are not only gaining experience with number relationships and estimation, but they are using that experience to solve problems. They are not only increasing their understanding of statistics as they understand the sports stats, but they are doing statistical investigations as they make conjectures, gather data, and discuss conclusions.

YSTM Is Easy to Use

On some blackline masters the sports statistics are provided. These blackline masters are self-contained and generally do not require a newspaper. Other blackline masters have the word *more* in the title. These are similar to the previous page, but allow students to insert their own up-to-date statistics from the newspaper or from other sources. A third type of blackline master also requires up-to-date statistics, but may not be the same as the previous page. Again a newspaper is a primary source but not the only source. All blackline masters encourage student-generated investigations.

YSTM Is for Girls and Boys

In the past, on hearing of the mixing of sports and math, some people have said, "What about the girls?" This is a very sexist question. There are some girls and some boys who are interested in a particular sport. There are some girls and some boys who are not interested in a particular sport. Interest, not gender, is the crucial issue.

The author has found that some students who profess lack of interest in a particular sport are actually unfamiliar with it and fear appearing stupid. A careful explanation of the sport's terms and statistics can often turn a "Who cares? This is boring" response into a willingness to try. The best person to give these explanations is another student.

YSTM Is for Sports Fans

We all long to be successful. Imagine you're the kid at the back of the room. You hate to answer questions in class. Everybody seems to get it. You don't. Your only wish is for the math class to be over. Your real interest is sports—playing and watching. With YSTM the teacher is asking you to explain a sports term to the class. That's easy. Don't they get it? You even explained a certain statistic to the kid at the front of the room. Maybe they're not so smart after all. Maybe you're smarter than you thought. Maybe you can do that other math. Success is the best motivator. For some kids, YSTM provides that initial success.

Suppose you're the kid at the front of the room. Math is a breeze, but boring. No problem. You'll play the game and get good marks. But this YSTM is always demanding more of you: "Explain—is that reasonable? What do I think? Why? What if? Discuss with a friend." You can even collect your own up-to-date stats and design your own investigations. YSTM is neat.

YSTM Is for Risk-Taking Teachers

YSTM is especially designed to encourage teachers who are not particularly interested in sports. The completed pages have all the needed examples, questions, data, and if appropriate, answers. These pages model the questions and answers so that the teacher can see exactly how the following page (without statistics) should be done with up-to-date data.

Nevertheless, it takes courage for a teacher who is unfamiliar or uninterested in sports to take a risk and use YSTM. Take a chance. Students learn more from our behavior than from our words. Demonstrate to your students the risk taking that you ask from them. Let your students teach you something. We are all lifelong learners. Students will appreciate you more for your efforts, not less. Become a partner to your students in discovering YSTM.

On the other hand, if you're a teacher who is a sports fan, you will probably enjoy YSTM as much as the students in your class.

YSTM Has a Range of Sports

YSTM has a range of sports. However, there is a heavy emphasis on basketball, baseball, football, and hockey. This is because these sports generally have the most statistics available in the newspaper. If statistics are available locally for other sports that are not included in YSTM, by all means apply the ideas in YSTM to these sports. Many of the YSTM ideas suggested for one sport apply to other sports. As with any teaching tool, the success of YSTM depends on the flexibility and good judgment of the teacher.

YSTM Is Made for Cooperative Learning

YSTM is a natural vehicle for cooperative learning in the classroom or in the family. With the students' interest in sports and with so much of YSTM content being student generated, lively discussion takes place. Therefore the social skills taught during cooperative learning come into play. Social skills such as taking turns, encouraging, listening, giving help, staying on task, all may be taught through YSTM. Leadership, decision making, and being a team player may all be learned during YSTM time. Jig-Saw and Think-Pair-Share are just two of the many cooperative learning structures that are very effective with YSTM. Many of the activities in YSTM involve collecting data. Small groups of students can work with different data and then compare their results with the other groups. As well, different groups can do different activities and then report to the class.

However, cooperative learning is just one method of using YSTM. Students can also enjoy YSTM when the teacher leads the activity in a more traditional setting or when YSTM is used at an activity center. YSTM can also be effective as independent study for some enthusiastic students.

Whatever your teaching style, the students will have fun and learn with YSTM.

YSTM Is Language, Too

At every grade level the NCTM Standards has communication as a goal in math class. On every blackline master, students are required to read and to listen as well as to talk and write—in short, to communicate. It's hard to tell where the math ends and the language begins. They're integrated.

In addition, YSTM has six pages with 24 ideas for integrating your language program with sports. All 24 ideas use the sports section of the newspaper as a source. Language learning is enhanced through the integration of sports and the newspaper.

Baseball

In 1927 Babe Ruth of the New York Yankees hit 60 home runs. This was an incredible feat. In fact, it was more home runs than any other team hit that year. That's right . . . any other TEAM.

American League Team Home Runs 1927

Boston	28
Chicago	36
Cleveland	26
Detroit	51
Philadelphia	56
St. Louis	5
Washington	29

Since 1900 fewer than ten players have hit four home runs in a single game. Only one, Mike Schmidt, hit four in four times up to bat.

Only one player in the National League has hit two home runs with the bases loaded in the same game. His name was Tony Cloninger. What makes this even more exceptional is that Cloninger was a pitcher.

Cal Ripken Jr. has played in more consecutive games than anybody in the history of baseball. In addition, he has hit more home runs than any other shortstop.

In July 1987 Don Mattingly set an American League record by hitting home runs in eight straight games. Ken Griffey Jr. matched his record in July 1993.

No team has matched the Toronto Blue Jays' 10 home runs in an 18 to 3 win against Baltimore in September 1987.

Scores and Puzzles

Use the clues to help you find the scores of these games.

1. The Tigers and the Brewers together scored 14 runs.
   The Tigers scored 10 runs.

   Tigers _____ , Brewers _____

2. The Phillies beat the Mets by five runs.
   Altogether 11 runs were scored.

   Phillies _____ , Mets _____

3. The Expos score three times as many runs as the Pirates.
   Altogether 12 runs were scored.

   Expos _____ , Pirates _____

4. The Rockies scored 3 runs.
   The Braves scored two more than twice as many runs as the Rockies.

   Braves _____ , Rockies _____

5. The White Sox and the A's together scored 7 runs.
   The A's scored 2 runs.

   White Sox _____ , A's _____

6. The Red Sox scored seven more runs than the Twins.
   The Red Sox scored 9 runs.

   Red Sox _____ , Twins _____

7. The Orioles and the Yankees together scored 11 runs.
   The Orioles won by one run.

   Orioles _____ , Yankees _____

8. The Dodgers and the Reds together scored 13 runs.
   The Dodgers scored two fewer than four times as many runs as the Reds.

   Dodgers _____ , Reds _____

Using scores from a recent newspaper, make up three Scores and Puzzles questions. Read the clues from one of your puzzles to a friend. See if your friend can give the final score without using paper and pencil.

Games of the Week

These are the scores of National League games during one week in a season.

Tuesday
Colorado 4, San Francisco 2
Florida 1, Pittsburgh 0
New York 3, Montreal 2 (10 innings)
St. Louis 7, Chicago 6 (11 innings)
Atlanta 9, Philadelphia 8 (15 innings)
Cincinnati 5, San Diego 0
Los Angeles 5, Houston 4 (10 innings)

Wednesday
Atlanta 4, Philadelphia 2
San Francisco 6, Colorado 1
Pittsburgh 5, Florida 1
Montreal 4, New York 3
St. Louis 3, Chicago 2
Los Angeles 1, Houston 0
Cincinnati 9, San Diego 5

Thursday
Chicago 8, St. Louis 6
Philadelphia 6, Pittsburgh 4

Friday
Chicago 6, Florida 4
Montreal 9, St. Louis 1
Philadelphia 12, Pittsburgh 1
Atlanta 7, New York 2
Houston 4, Colorado 2
Los Angeles 5, San Diego 4
San Francisco 9, Cincinnati 5

Saturday
St. Louis 6, Montreal 3
New York 11, Atlanta 4
Florida 6, Chicago 4
San Francisco 3, Cincinnati 1
Philadelphia 3, Pittsburgh 2
Colorado 4, Houston 2
Los Angeles 2, San Diego 1

Sunday
Montreal 9, St. Louis 8
Philadelphia 1, Pittsburgh 0
Atlanta 6, New York 1
Florida 3, Chicago 0
Colorado 4, Houston 0
Los Angeles 7, San Diego 1
Cincinnati 9, San Francisco 6 (10 innings)

Monday
Pittsburgh 7, St. Louis 2
Montreal 4, Philadelphia 1
Florida 3, New York 1
Chicago 4, San Diego 2
Houston 3, San Francisco 2
Los Angeles 9, Colorado 2

Use the scores to help you answer these questions about the week.

1. What was the most popular score?

2. Is the difference between the winning and losing teams most often
   A. 1 run   B. 2 runs
   C. 3 runs   D. more than 3 runs

3. Extra innings occurs about one game in
   A. 5   B. 10
   C. 15   D. 20

4. Find the number of days when two games had the same score.

5. Which was the highest scoring day? Why?

6. Which was the lowest scoring day? Why?

7. Create your own question from these scores and share it with the class.

More Games of the Week

Scores

Collect a week's worth of baseball scores from a newspaper.

Attach them to or copy them in the left-hand column.

These scores could be from hardball or softball games in any league—professional, amateur, or school.

Use the scores to help you answer these questions about that week.

1. What was the most popular score?

2. Is the difference between the winning and losing teams most often
   A. 1 run   B. 2 runs
   C. 3 runs   D. more than 3 runs

3. Extra innings occur in about 1 game in
   A. 5   B. 10
   C. 15   D. 20

4. Find the number of days when two games had the same score.

5. Which was the highest scoring day? Why?

6. Which was the lowest scoring day? Why?

7. Create your own question from these scores and share it with the class.

Classic Games

Use the clues to help you complete the inning-by-inning summaries of these two memorable games.

Game 1 Clues

- The Phillies scored five more runs in the eighth inning than they did in the second inning.

- In the second inning, the Cubs scored seven more runs than the Phillies.

- The Phillies scored seven fewer runs in the fourth inning than in the eighth inning.

- In the fourth inning, 15 runs were scored.

- At the end of five innings, the Cubs led 25 to 9.

- The Phillies scored as many runs in the ninth inning as they did in the second, third, and fourth innings.

Team	1	2	3	4	5	6	7	8	9	Final Score
Phillies	0	3	2	—	—	0	0	—	—	—
Cubs	1	—	—	—	0	1	0	0	x —	—

Game 2 Clues

- The Red Sox scored 23 runs.

- In the sixth inning, three runs were scored, with the Tigers scoring one less run than the Red Sox.

- The Tigers scored as many runs in the fourth inning as the Red Sox did in the sixth inning.

- The Red Sox scored as many runs in the second inning as the Tigers did the whole game.

- The Red Sox scored half as many runs in the eighth inning as they did in the sixth inning.

Team	1	2	3	4	5	6	7	8	9	Final Score
Tigers	0	0	0	—	0	—	0	0	0 —	—
Red Sox	0	—	0	0	0	—	—	—	x —	—

The *x* means that the home team did not bat in the bottom of the ninth inning because they had already won the game.

Why do you think these games are memorable?

For help in reading the inning-by-inning summary, see "How to Read an Inning-by-Inning Summary" (page 17).

More Classic Games

To create a Classic Games puzzle of your own, you will need the inning-by-inning summary of a game.

The game could be a local softball or hardball game or a major league game.

Inning-by-inning summaries for major league games are found in most newspapers.

On a separate piece of paper, copy the inning-by-inning summary of the game you have chosen.

On this page fill in part of the inning-by-inning summary, but leave part of the summary blank.

List clues that would help a friend complete the missing parts of the summary.

See if a friend can complete the inning-by-inning summary, using these clues.

Team	1	2	3	4	Inning 5	6	7	8	9	Final Score
_____	____	____	____	____	____	____	____	____	____	____
_____	____	____	____	____	____	____	____	____	____	____

Clues

_____

_____

_____

_____

_____

_____

_____

For help in reading an inning-by-inning summary see "How to Read an Inning-by-Inning Summary" (page 17).

Who Will Win?

Does the team that scores first go on to win the game?

A. almost always
B. much more often than not
C. about half the time
D. once in a while
E. never

Share your guess with a friend. To check the accuracy of your guess, use the inning-by-inning summaries below.

To help you collect the data, circle the winning team and box the team that scored first. In what fraction of the games did the team that scored first, win the game? Are you surprised?

1. Seattle	0	0	0	0	0	1	0	0	1—2					
New York	0	0	0	2	0	0	2	0	x—4					
2. Montreal	2	0	0	1	2	0	0	0	0—5					
San Diego	0	1	1	0	0	0	0	2	0—4					
3. California	2	0	0	0	2	3	0	0	0—7					
Detroit	0	0	1	2	0	2	0	0	0—5					
4. St. Louis	1	0	0	0	0	0	0	0	0—1					
Colorado	0	2	3	0	0	1	0	4	x—10					
5. Cleveland	2	0	0	0	0	0	1	2	0—5					
Boston	3	8	0	0	0	2	0	0	x—13					
6. Houston	0	0	0	2	0	1	2	1	1—7					
Pittsburgh	0	1	0	0	0	0	1	2	0—4					
7. San Francisco	3	0	0	1	0	0	0	0	2—6					
New York	0	0	0	0	0	1	4	0	0—5					
8. Los Angeles	0	2	0	4	2	1	0	0	1—10					
Montreal	2	0	0	0	0	0	0	2	0—4					
9. Chicago	0	0	2	2	1	0	0	0	0	1	0	2—8		
Milwaukee	0	2	0	1	2	0	0	0	0	1	0	0—6		
10. Seattle	1	2	0	0	0	0	0	0	3—6					
Boston	1	0	5	0	1	0	0	0	x—7					
11. Kansas City	0	0	0	0	0	0	0	0	0—0					
Toronto	0	0	0	1	0	0	0	0	x—1					
12. California	0	1	0	1	4	2	0	3	0—11					
Baltimore	0	0	1	0	0	0	1	1	5—8					
13. Cincinnati	2	8	0	1	2	1	0	0	0—14					
Colorado	0	0	2	0	0	0	2	0	0—4					

14. Texas	0	0	0	0	0	1	0	2	0	0	0—3			
Toronto	0	0	0	3	0	0	0	0	0	0	1—4			
15. New York	0	1	0	2	0	2	1	4	0	0	0	0	0—10	
Pittsburgh	0	0	0	3	0	5	1	0	1	0	0	0	1—11	
16. Cleveland	0	0	0	0	0	0	0	1	0—1					
Chicago	0	1	4	0	2	2	0	3	x—12					
17. San Diego	1	0	0	0	2	3	1	0	1—8					
Philadelphia	2	0	1	0	0	0	0	0	0—3					
18. Minnesota	2	0	1	1	0	0	0	1	1—6					
Milwaukee	3	0	0	0	4	0	0	0	x—7					
19. Cleveland	3	1	0	1	0	0	4	0	1—10					
Minnesota	0	3	1	0	0	1	1	0	0—6					
20. Florida	0	2	0	1	0	3	0	0	0—6					
Atlanta	0	1	0	0	0	0	2	0	0—3					
21. Texas	0	0	0	0	1	0	0	0	0—1					
Kansas City	0	0	0	0	0	0	3	0	x—3					
22. New York	0	0	0	3	0	0	2	0	0	0	0—5			
Los Angeles	1	0	0	0	1	2	1	0	0	0	1—6			
23. Cincinnati	0	3	1	0	0	1	0	0	0—5					
Chicago	0	0	0	2	0	0	0	0	0—2					
24. Oakland	0	0	1	4	0	0	0	0	0—5					
Boston	0	0	0	0	0	4	0	0	2—6					
25. Texas	0	0	2	1	3	0	0	0	1—7					
Detroit	0	1	0	0	0	0	0	1	0—2					

With the help of a partner, create another investigation based on these inning-by-inning summaries.

For help in reading an inning-by-inning summary see "How to Read an Inning-by-Inning Summary" (page 17).

More Who Will Win?

Score Summaries

Does the team that scores first go on to win the game?

A. almost always   D. once in a while

B. more often than not   E. never

C. about half the time

Many students were surprised with the answer they found to this question when they used the data provided on "Who Will Win?" (page 7).

Maybe your data will give a different result.

From a newspaper collect inning-by-inning summaries from at least 25 games. Why would it be good to use summaries from 25 or more games?

Attach the summaries to this page.

To help you use the data

• Circle the winning team.

• Box the team that scored first.

In what fraction of the games did the team that scored first win the game?

Are you surprised?

With the help of a partner, create another investigation based on these inning-by-inning summaries.

In baseball, batting average is referred to more than any other statistic. It is often used to compare hitters—the higher the batting average, the better the hitter.

This information is taken from a boxscore of a Dodgers' game.

Players	ab	h	avg
Butler	5	4	_____
DeShields	4	2	_____
Piazza	3	2	_____
Wallach	4	1	_____
Rodriguez	2	1	_____
Karros	4	0	_____
Mondesi	4	2	_____
Offerman	3	1	_____
Astocio	3	0	_____

1. Find the batting average for each player. Complete the batting average column.

2. How many different batting averages did you find?

3. Which player had the most hits?

4. Which player had the highest batting average?

5. Try to find two players with different batting averages, but the same number of hits.

6. Find two players with the same batting average, but a different number of hits.

7. Why is batting average a better way to compare players than just comparing the number of hits.

8. What was the team batting average?

For help in calculating a batting average, see "How to Calculate a Batting Average" (page 18).

More It's a Hit

From a newspaper, choose a boxscore of a game in which your favorite team played. Copy the information into the partial boxscore below. Use your school team stats if they're available!

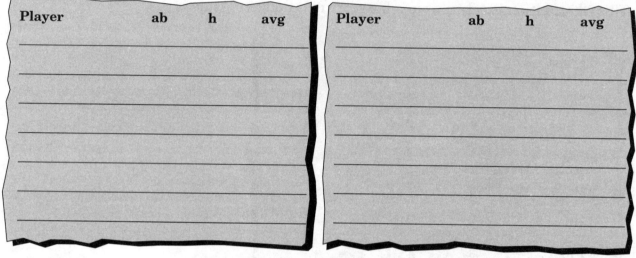

Player	ab	h	avg

Player	ab	h	avg

1. Find the batting average for each player. Complete the batting average column.

2. How many different batting averages did you find?

3. Which player had the most hits?

4. Which player had the highest batting average?

5. Find two players with different batting averages, but the same number of hits.

6. Find two players with the same batting average, but a different number of hits.

7. What was the team batting average?

8. Collect at least three boxscores of games involving your favorite team. Find the player with the highest batting average for the three games. Compare your results with a friend.

9. Consider all the boxscores from games played on a single day. Which team had the highest batting average?

For help in calculating a batting average, see "How to Calculate a Batting Average" (page 18). For help in reading a boxscore, see "How to Read a Boxscore (Hitters)" (page 19).

A hitter's power is often measured by a statistic called slugging average. Slugging average is found by dividing total bases by times at bat. Total bases are made up of 1 base for each single, 2 bases for each double, 3 bases for each triple, and 4 bases for each home run.

$$\text{Slugging Average} = \frac{\text{Total Bases}}{\text{At Bats}}$$

Total Bases $= 1 \times s + 2 \times d + 3 \times t + 4 \times h$

For example, from a boxscore we find this information on Barry Bonds.

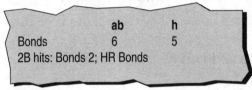

	ab	h
Bonds	6	5
2B hits: Bonds 2; HR Bonds		

This means that Bonds had 2 doubles, 0 triples, and 1 home run. Therefore Bonds had 2 singles.

Bonds' slugging average in this game was

$$\text{Slugging Average} = \frac{2 \times 1 + 2 \times 2 + 0 \times 3 + 1 \times 4}{6}$$

$$= \frac{10}{6}$$

$$= 1.667$$

Some Slugging Explorations from the Newspaper

• Find a boxscore for a game involving your favorite team.

• Which player had the highest slugging average? What was it?

• Compare the slugging average over a week for two of baseball's top hitters.

• On a given day, which player in the major leagues had the best slugging average?

Create your own slugging average exploration.

Pitching Performances

A pitcher is often judged by his earned run average, era. The smaller the era, the better the pitcher. Greg Maddux finished the 1994 season with an incredible 1.56 era. This means that over a nine-inning game, on average, Maddux allowed only a little over $1\frac{1}{2}$ runs.

Here is the formula for calculating a pitcher's earned run average.

$$\text{Earned Run Average} = \frac{\text{Earned Runs Allowed} \times 9}{\text{Innings Pitched}}$$

In the example used in "How to Read a Boxscore (Pitchers)" (page 20) Maddux allowed 2 earned runs in 7 innings.

Therefore his earned run average in this game was

$$\frac{2 \times 9}{7} = \frac{18}{7} = 2.57.$$

This pitching information is taken from the boxscore of an All Star game.

Pitchers	ip	er	era
Martinez	2	1	_____
Ontiveros	$\frac{2}{3}$	1	_____
Nomo	1	0	_____
Rogers	1	1	_____
Smiley	2	2	_____

1. Find each pitcher's earned run average. Complete the era column.

2. Which pitcher allowed the most earned runs?

3. Which pitcher had the highest era?
   Could you have predicted this without actually calculating his era?

4. Why is it fairer to compare pitchers using their era's, rather than the number of games each won?

More Pitching Performances

Choose a newspaper that has boxscores of baseball games from both the American League and the National League. From your favorite league, cut out all the boxscores that are available. Make sure everybody in your class has a copy of these boxscores.

For the games played on this one day only

1. Which starting pitcher had the highest era?

Name _____ ip _____ er _____ era _____

2. Which relief pitcher had the highest era?

Name _____ ip _____ er _____ era _____

As a long-term project, select the Relief Pitcher of the Week. After studying boxscores for a week, select a relief pitcher with a small era over that week, but who pitched a reasonable number of innings. Write a brief report, including stats, to convince your class that you have made a reasonable choice. Compare your choice for Relief Pitcher of the Week with those of your classmates.

Who's in First?

Take a look at the team standings in the newspaper. One column is under the title GB, which stands for games behind the leader. For example,

	Wins	Losses	GB
San Francisco	16	13	—
Los Angeles	12	17	4

Los Angeles is four games behind San Francisco. This means that if Los Angeles won four games and San Francisco lost four games, the teams would be tied.

The calculation of GB involves the difference in wins and the difference in losses.

Figure out how GB is calculated from these two examples.

	W	L	GB
Cincinnati	22	16	—
Houston	15	23	7

$$\frac{(22-15)+(23-16)}{2}$$

	W	L	GB
Atlanta	20	11	—
Montreal	16	14	$3\frac{1}{2}$

$$\frac{(20-16)+(14-11)}{2}$$

1. Find the GB for Chicago and Oakland

	W	L	GB
Cleveland	36	21	—
Chicago	32	27	_____

	W	L	GB
California	48	44	—
Oakland	41	54	_____

2. In this GB column some of the answers are right, some are wrong. Correct the ones that are wrong.

	W	L	GB
Boston	13	5	—
New York	12	6	1
Toronto	13	8	3
Baltimore	9	11	4
Detroit	5	16	$9\frac{1}{2}$

Copy the baseball standings from a newspaper, but omit the GB column. Have a partner complete the missing GB column.

You're the Manager

This is your chance to predict who will be the best hitters in a future game. You're the manager. As a class, choose your favorite baseball team. Who in the class can pick five players who will have the highest batting average in a future game?

Here are the steps to follow for this activity.

1. Choose a future date when your favorite team will be playing.

2. Before that game has been played, select five hitters from your favorite team. Write their names on the chart below. A newspaper will tell you how each player is hitting this season.

   Some students may prefer to work with partners or in small groups when selecting the players.

3. After the chosen game, record on the chart the at bats and hits for these five players. This information will be in the boxscore found in a newspaper.

   See "How to Read a Boxscore (Hitters)" (page 19).

4. Add up the at bats and add up the hits. Then, from these totals, calculate your team's batting average.

   See "How to Calculate a Batting Average" (page 18).

5. Who in the class had the highest batting average? Who was the best manager in the class?

6. Another way to do this activity is to allow the five hitters to be chosen from a variety of teams.

Players	ab	h	Batting Average
Totals			

In "Who Will Win?" inning-by-inning summaries were used to explore whether the team that scores first usually goes on to win the game. Here are some other questions to explore using inning-by-inning summaries.

• In which inning is the first run of the game scored?

• Does the winning team score more runs in one inning than the losing team does in the whole game?

• If the home team scores first, does it win the game?

• For extra-inning games, does the team that scored last in the first nine innings win?

A boxscore was used with "It's a Hit" and "The Sluggers." More explorations using a boxscore could include these questions.

• Which is a better indicator of the winning team, the team with more stolen bases or the team with fewer errors?

• Consider all the boxscores in the newspaper on a single day. Find the team that had the most players with a higher batting average in that one game than they had for the entire season.

• For your favorite team, copy each player's name and batting average on a separate file card.

  Shuffle the file cards.

  Give each file card to a different person.

  Have the students line up from highest batting average to lowest.

Using a boxscore, explore these pitching statistics.

• On average, how many pitchers are used by the winning team? losing team?

• For a winning pitcher, what is the ratio of strikeouts to walks?

• Who has a lower era—starting pitchers or relief pitchers?

Add your own ideas for exploration.

How to Read an Inning-by-Inning Summary

On October 20, 1993, Toronto Blue Jays and Philadelphia Phillies set a World Series record when they scored 29 runs. The Blue Jays won 15 to 14.

Here is the scoring in that game, inning by inning.

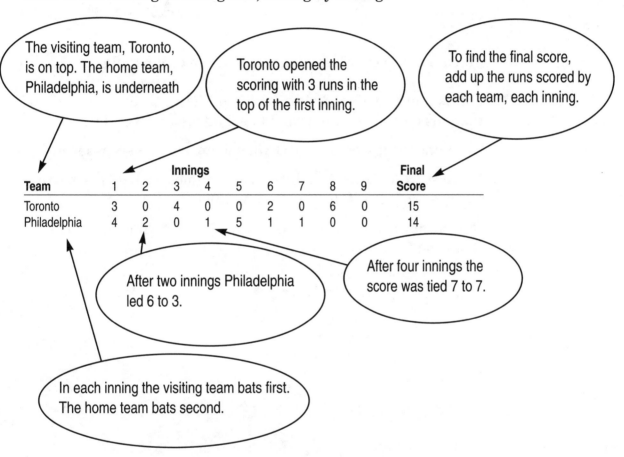

The visiting team, Toronto, is on top. The home team, Philadelphia, is underneath

Toronto opened the scoring with 3 runs in the top of the first inning.

To find the final score, add up the runs scored by each team, each inning.

Team	Innings 1	2	3	4	5	6	7	8	9	Final Score
Toronto	3	0	4	0	0	2	0	6	0	15
Philadelphia	4	2	0	1	5	1	1	0	0	14

After two innings Philadelphia led 6 to 3.

After four innings the score was tied 7 to 7.

In each inning the visiting team bats first. The home team bats second.

In the newspaper this summary would be shortened to read

Toronto	3	0	4	0	0	2	0	6	0—15
Philadelphia	4	2	0	1	5	1	1	0	0—14

How to Calculate a Batting Average

To calculate a hitter's batting average, take the number of hits, h, and divide by the number of times the hitter was at bat, ab. (If a hitter is hit by a pitch, walks, or has a sacrifice, this does not count as a time at bat.)

$$\text{Batting Average} = \frac{\text{Hits}}{\text{At Bats}}$$

The answer is expressed, correct to three decimal places.

For example, if Ken Griffey had two hits in three times at bat, then his batting average would be 2 divided by 3 or .667.

The announcer would say, "Griffey is hitting six, sixty-seven."

If Moises Alou had four hits in four times at bat, his batting average would be 4 divided by 4 or 1.000.

The announcer in this case would say, "Alou is batting a thousand."

How to Read a Boxscore (Hitters)

The boxscore of a game uses shorthand to describe how each player did in that game. Once you know the shorthand, it is easy to interpret the boxscore.

This is part of a boxscore from a Yankees' game.

Boxscore (Hitters) New York	AB	R	H	BI	BB	SO	AVG
Polonia lf	5	0	1	0	0	1	.282
Velarde 3b	5	1	1	1	0	1	.265
Mattingly 1b	5	1	1	0	0	0	.322
Tartabull dh	5	1	1	0	0	3	.239
O'Neill rf	4	1	3	1	1	1	.475
Leyritz c	5	1	2	3	0	1	.293
Boston cf	3	0	0	0	1	0	.129
Gallego ss	3	0	0	0	1	1	.218
Kelly 2b	3	0	0	0	1	1	.295
Totals	38	5	9	5	4	9	

A number in parentheses indicates the number so far this season.

LOB — New York 7. 2B, O'Neill (12). HR — Velarde (2), O'Neill (10), Leyritz (7). RBIs — Velarde (11), O'Neill (35), Leyritz 3 (20). SB — Kelly (1).

DP — New York 1 (Gallego, Kelly, and Mattingly).

Baseball has its own language or terminology. Check with a class expert on what each of the terms means. Test your boxscore reading ability by checking these true statements.

- Left fielder Mike Polonia had one hit in five times at bat.

- Don Mattingly's batting average was .322 so far that season.

- Danny Tartabull struck out 3 times this game.

- One of Paul O'Neill's hits was a double, his 12th of the season. Another hit was a home run, his tenth of the season. Since he had no triples, his third hit must have been a 1B hit or single.

- Jim Leyritz had three runs batted in, his 18th, 19th, and 20th of the season.

Positions

lf—left field
cf—center field
rf—right field
3b—third base
ss—shortstop
2b—second base
1b—first base
c—catcher
p—pitcher
dh—designated hitter
ph—pinch hitter
pr—pinch runner

Other abbreviations

AB—at bats, times at bat
R—runs scored
H—hits
BI—runs batted in
BB—bases on balls, walks
SO—strikeouts
AVG—batting average, so far in the season
E—errors
LOB—runners left on base
2B—two-base hits, doubles
3B—three-base hits, triples
HR—home runs
RBI—runs batted in
SB—stolen bases
CS—caught stealing
S—sacrifices
SF—sacrifice flies
GIDP—grounded into double plays
DP—double plays

How to Read a Boxscore (Pitchers)

How each pitcher did in a game shows up in the boxscore. Learn the boxscore shorthand and learn about the game's pitchers.

IP—innings pitched
H—hits
R—runs
ER—earned runs
BB—base on balls, walks
SO—strikeouts

NP—number of pitches thrown
ERA—earned run average, so far this season
IBB—intentional bases on balls
HPB—batter hit by pitcher
WP—wild pitch
PB—passed ball

Check with a class expert to learn more about these terms.

The first pitcher listed for each team is the starting pitcher. All the rest are relief pitchers, listed in the order of their appearance. If a relief pitcher enters the game with runners on the bases, we say these are inherited runners. Each out a pitcher gets counts as 1/3 of an inning.

Atlanta	IP	H	R	ER	BB	SO	NP	ERA
G. Maddux W, 7-2	7	5	2	2	3	9	113	1.37
Wohlers	0	3	1	1	0	0	11	4.91
Bedrosian	1	0	0	0	0	1	7	5.51
McMichael	1	0	0	0	1	1	22	2.49
Colorado	**IP**	**H**	**R**	**ER**	**BB**	**SO**	**NP**	**ERA**
Painter L, 0-7	$3\frac{2}{3}$	7	6	6	1	0	65	14.73
Blair	$1\frac{1}{3}$	0	0	0	0	2	21	7.36

Test your boxscore reading ability by checking these true statements.

• Greg Maddux was the starting pitcher for Atlanta. He pitched seven innings and was the winning pitcher. It was his seventh win of the season against only two losses. After this game his era this season was 1.37.

• Steve Bedrosian was the third Atlanta pitcher. He pitched one inning. It took him only seven pitches to get the three outs.

• Lance Painter was the Colorado starting pitcher. He was replaced with two out in the fourth inning.

• Atlanta pitchers struck out 11 Colorado batters.

SECTION 2
• •
Football

On November 8, 1970, Tom Dempsey kicked a field goal on the last play of the game to give New Orleans a 19 to 17 win over Detroit. Dempsey's kick went 63 yards. It was his fourth field goal of the game. He became a great field goal kicker despite being born with part of his kicking foot missing.

NFL Scores
Jets 23, Bills 3
Lions 31, Falcons 28
Browns 28, Bengals 20
Colts 45, Oilers 21
Chiefs 30, Saints 17
Packers 16, Vikings 10
Giants 28, Eagles 23
Seahawks 28, Redskins 7
Bears 21, Buccaneers 9
Rams 14, Cardinals 12
Cowboys 26, Steelers 9
Dolphins 39, Patriots 35
Chargers 37, Broncos 34

If you rounded all the scores to the nearest ten, would this affect the standings?

On November 27, 1966, the Giants beat the Redskins 72 to 41.

"And so far in the first quarter Troy Aikman is perfect, completing seven out of eight passes."— broadcaster Jack Buck during a Cowboys playoff game.

The telecast of Super Bowl XXVII took 3 hours, 23 minutes, 5 seconds.

Commercials took 43 minutes, 30 seconds.

Actual playing time (snap to whistle) was only 15 minutes 42 seconds.

Weekend Games

Use the clues to help you figure out the scores of these weekend football games.

1. The Browns lost by 17 points.
    The Seahawks scored 22 points.

    Browns _____

    Seahawks _____

2. The Redskins scored 6 points.
    The Giants won by 14 points.

    Giants _____

    Redskins _____

3. The Packers and the Saints together scored 36 points.
    The Packers edged the Saints by 2 points.

    Saints _____

    Packers _____

4. The Chiefs beat the Raiders by 11 points.
    Together they scored 51 points.

    Raiders _____

    Chiefs _____

5. The 49ers scored 3 more than twice as many points as the Buccaneers.
    The Buccaneers scored 21 points.

    Buccaneers _____

    49ers _____

6. The Cardinals scored 5 more than half of what the Cowboys scored.
    The Cowboys scored 20 points.

    Cardinals _____

    Cowboys _____

Using football scores from a recent weekend, make up some Weekend Games puzzles. The games could be high school, college, or professional. Read your clues to the class and see if they can tell you the scores of the games.

Here are one day's scores from the National Football League.

Teams and Scores	Total Points Scored
1. Bills 10, Eagles 7	_____
2. Patriots 7, Bengals 2	_____
3. Oilers 19, Browns 17	_____
4. Giants 20, Colts 6	_____
5. Packers 20, Chargers 13	_____
6. Raiders 27, Seahawks 23	_____
7. Lions 21, Cardinals 14	_____
8. Broncos 27, Chiefs 21	_____
9. Cowboys 37, Vikings 20	_____
10. Rams 23, Saints 20	_____
11. Jets 3, Redskins 0	_____
12. Falcons 27, 49ers 24	_____
13. Buccaneers 13, Bears 10	_____

1. Find the number of points scored in each game and complete the chart.

2. What was the highest scoring game?

3. What was the lowest scoring game?

4. In what percent of the games were 40 or more points scored?

5. In what percent of the games were under 20 points scored?

Score Search

Study the sports section of a Monday newspaper. Consider high school, college, and professional games. What is the highest scoring game you can find?

More High and Low

Use a Monday newspaper to find the scores of 13 National Football League games.

Write in the teams and the scores below.

Teams	Game Scores	Total Points Scored

Find the number of points scored in each game and complete the chart.

- What was the highest scoring game?

- What was the lowest scoring game?

- In what percent of the games were 40 or more points scored?

- In what percent of the games were under 20 points scored?

- How do your answers compare to the answers to High and Low?

Continue this activity for a number of weeks and look for patterns.

Try this activity with college or high school football games and compare your answers.

Comebacks

How often does a team trail at halftime, but make a comeback in the third and fourth quarters to win the football game?

To answer this question, use these summaries from a week in the National Football League.

- Circle the winning team.

- Put a check beside the team that was losing at halftime.

- In what percent of the games was the second-half comeback successful? Are you surprised?

Quarter-by-Quarter Scoring Summaries

	Team	Q1	Q2	Q3	Q4		Total
1.	Redskins	3	0	3	0	—	6
	Rams	0	0	0	10	—	10
2.	Vikings	0	7	3	0	—	10
	Buccaneers	3	3	10	7	—	23
3.	Lions	0	10	7	0	—	17
	Packers	10	3	3	10	—	26
4.	Steelers	0	0	6	7	—	13
	Broncos	10	10	14	3	—	37
5.	Raiders	3	3	3	3	—	12
	Chargers	0	0	0	7	—	7
6.	Giants	0	0	0	7	—	7
	Eagles	0	0	3	0	—	3
7.	Patriots	3	0	3	7	—	13
	Dolphins	0	0	3	14	—	17
8.	Colts	3	3	3	0	—	9
	Bills	0	16	7	0	—	23
9.	Oilers	0	14	3	10	—	27
	Browns	3	7	0	10	—	20
10.	Cowboys	0	0	7	7	—	14
	Falcons	3	10	7	7	—	27
11.	Bears	0	6	6	7	—	19
	Chiefs	7	7	3	0	—	17
12.	Bengals	3	0	0	9	—	12
	Jets	0	14	0	3	—	17

For help in reading these summaries, see "How to Read a Quarter-by-Quarter Scoring Summary" (page 31).

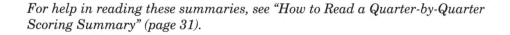

More Comebacks

Quarter-by-Quarter Scoring Summaries

How often does a team trail at halftime but make a comeback in the third and fourth quarters to win the football game?

This time to answer the question, collect your own quarter-by-quarter scoring summaries.

They could be from high school, college, or professional games. The newspaper or a school coach would be a good source for this data.

- Copy on this page a number of quarter-by-quarter summaries. Discuss with a friend what a reasonable number might be.

- Circle the winning team.

- Put a check beside the team that was losing at halftime.

- In what percent of the games was the second half comeback successful? How does this answer compare with the answer in "Comebacks"?

- Which answer is more reasonable? Why?

For help in reading these summaries, see "How to Read a Quarter-by-Quarter Scoring Summary" (page 31).

Passing Fancy

In the newspaper is a summary of individual statistics that shows the quarterbacks passing achievements in a game. For example, in one game it read

> Aikman 19 - 29 - 1 - 208

This means that Troy Aikman threw 29 passes, completed 19, had 1 intercepted, and that his passes gained 208 yards.

Aikman's pass-completion percent was $\frac{19}{29}$ = 65.5%.

From a Monday newspaper, collect from weekend games the passing stats for at least 10 quarterbacks.

Which three quarterbacks had the best pass completion percents? How many passes do you think a quarterback should throw in order to qualify for the top three? Why?

Since 1973, the National Football League has rated passers using this formula.

Pass Rating = $\frac{5}{6}$ (%C + 4 × %TD + 5 × AY + 2.5 − 5 × %I)

%C   percent of attempted passes that were completed.

%TD   percent of attempted passes that were touchdowns

AY   average yards gained on each attempted pass

%I   percent of attempted passes that were intercepted

In Aikman's case he also had one touchdown pass, so his rating is

%C = $\frac{19}{29}$ = 65.5; %TD = $\frac{1}{29}$ = 3.4; AY = $\frac{208}{29}$ = 7.2; %I = $\frac{1}{29}$ = 3.4

Substitute Aikman's stats into the formula to see that his pass rating in that game was 83.8.

What is the name of your favorite quarterback—pro or amateur?

Find his pass rating for a game.

Statistics for individual ball carriers in a game are listed in the newspaper under Rushing.

For example, Smith 19 - 104 means that, in one game, Emmitt Smith carried the ball 19 times and gained 104 yards.

Therefore Smith gained an average of $\frac{104}{19}$ = 5.5 yards per carry.

From a Monday newspaper, collect the rushing statistics from weekend games for at least 10 ball carriers. Complete the chart.

Decide how you will choose the top performer. Is it by the number of carries, the yardage gained, or the yards gained per carry? Discuss this with a friend. Who was the top performer? Why?

Player	Carries	Yards	Yards per Carry

Create a similar activity to find the top performing pass receiver.

Winning Secrets

Some newspapers publish detailed summaries of team statistics for certain games. This is part of one such summary.

New England Patriots 31 at Cincinati Bengals 28		
Team Statistics	**Patriots**	**Bengals**
1. First downs	28	21
2. Rushes-yards	36-82	20-99
3. Passing	365	219
4. Comp-Att-Int	30-50-2	21-29-0

The Patriots gained 365 yards passing.

The Patriot runners carried the ball 36 times and gained 82 yards.

This was an average of $\frac{82}{36}$ = 2.3 yards per carry.

The Bengals threw 29 passes, completed 21, and had none intercepted.

The Bengals passing completion average was $\frac{21}{29}$ = 72%.

From the newspaper, clip out team summaries for at least a dozen games.

• Which of the four categories most frequently indicates who won the game?

• Is a combination of some of these categories an even better indicator? How would this affect your coaching?

• In the team summaries you clipped out, are there other categories that might indicate the winner?

Other Football Investigations

A newspaper will be able to help you explore these questions.

- Is the winning margin usually less than a touchdown?

- Is it an advantage to be the home team?

- Which is the highest scoring quarter? half?

- Does the winning team score first?

- Does the winning team lead at the end of the first quarter? third quarter?

- Which football games have the highest scores—high school, college, or professional?

How to Read a Quarter-by-Quarter Summary

Scoring in a football game is broken down into four quarters (with halftime at the end of the second quarter). Add up the points in each quarter to find the final score.

For example

		Quarter			
	1st	2d	3d	4th	Final Score
Chiefs	0	7	14	10 —	31
Raiders	7	10	0	3 —	20

The Chiefs scored seven points in the second quarter.

In the second half, the Chiefs rallied for 14 + 10 = 24 points.

In the fourth quarter 10 + 3 = 13 points were scored.

The home team is on the bottom, so we know that the Raiders were the home team.

In the first half, the Raiders scored 7 + 10 = 17 points.

The Chiefs scored 0 + 7 + 14 = 21 points by the end of the third quarter.

In the newspaper, the summary for this game would appear like this.

Chiefs	0	7	14	10 — 31
Raiders	7	10	0	3 — 20

SECTION 3

Basketball

April 14, 1993
IF I HAD A MILLION DOLLARS Don Calhoun was picked from the crowd to try a shot from the opposite foul line—73 feet away from the basket. This was a promotional stunt during a time out at a Bulls–Heat basketball game.

The reward for a successful shot? $1,000,000. What were the chances? Calhoun dribbled once and then threw the ball baseball style. It was a bull's-eye—nothing but net. Don Calhoun was one million dollars richer. "I stepped up to the line with a lot of confidence," said Calhoun, a twenty-three-year-old office supply salesman from Bloomington, Illinois.

"I kept telling myself this was a once-in-a-lifetime shot, not to think about the money at all, just concentrate on the shot. Somehow I knew."

January 9, 1991
College student Michelle Jones scored 15 three-point baskets in one game.

February 25, 1924
Marie Boyd scored 156 points, nearly 94% of the points scored, as Central High School defeated Ursaline Academy, Cumbria, 163 to 3.

March 2, 1962
Wilt Chamberlain scored 100 points. Chamberlain made 36 out of 63 field goal attempts and 28 out of 32 foul shots to lead Philadelphia to a 169 to 147 win against New York.

June 25, 1977
Ted Martin demonstrated his foul-shot shooting ability by sinking 2036 consecutive foul shots.

Last Night's Scores

Here are some scores from women's college basketball.

Scores			
Tennessee	75,	Georgia	59
Colorado	89,	Oklahoma	79
North Carolina	91,	Clemson	86
Virginia	81,	North Carolina State	58
Purdue	76,	Northwestern	61
Seton Hall	73,	Georgetown	51
Penn State	96,	Ohio State	74
Southern Cal	99,	California	81
Stanford	94,	UCLA	82
Texas Tech	92,	Rice	70
Louisiana Tech	87,	Western Kentucky	82
Indiana	72,	Illinois	69
Boise State	74,	Montana State	53
Auburn	80,	Florida	76

1. Which team scored the most points?

2. Which team scored the fewest points?

3. In which game were the most points scored?

4. In which game were the fewest points scored?

5. Which game had the closest score?

6. Which game had the greatest winning margin?

More Last Night's Scores

Cut out the scores of recent basketball games from a newspaper. These scores could be from the NBA (National Basketball Association), college or high school, or from a local league. Tape or copy the scores onto the page. Then answer the questions.

Scores

1. Which team scored the most points?

2. Which team scored the fewest points?

3. In which game were the most points scored?

4. In which game were the fewest points scored?

5. Which game had the closest score?

6. Which game had the greatest winning margin?

Winning Margin

Scores

Long Beach State	82	
San Jose State	66	
Santa Barbara	73	
Pacific	66	
Oklahoma State	77	
Oklahoma	68	
Trinity	61	
Oglethorpe	60	
Mercy	80	
Queen's College	73	
DePaul	69	
Dayton	54	
Mount Mercy	63	
Rosary	49	
Kansas	64	
Nebraska	56	
Northwestern	89	
Minnesota	63	
Western Kentucky	77	
Lamar	54	
Washington	76	
Emory	73	
Tulane	77	
Louisville	62	
Sewanee	49	
Hendrix	48	
Roanoake	90	
Randolph-Macon	38	
Richmond	73	
William & Mary	56	
Old Dominion	73	
Madison	59	
Marymount	80	
Southwestern	78	
Boston College	90	
Providence	84	
Dickinson	70	
Wesley	62	
LeMoyne	80	
New Haven	75	

In women's college basketball, New Mexico beat Fresno State 57 to 53. This was a winning margin of four points.

Do you think most games are close, that they are decided by a small winning margin?

To help you answer the question, you have been given the scores of 20 games. Beside each game is a square. Fill in the square with the winning margin. Complete the tally chart below.

Winning Margin	Number of Games	Total
1–5 points		
6–10 points		
11–15 points		
16–20 points		
21–25 points		
26 or more points		
		20

After defining a *small winning margin,* write a paragraph supporting your answer to the question of whether most games are decided by a small winning margin.

Cut out the scores of some recent basketball games from a newspaper. The scores could be from any league: amateur or professional, women's or men's.

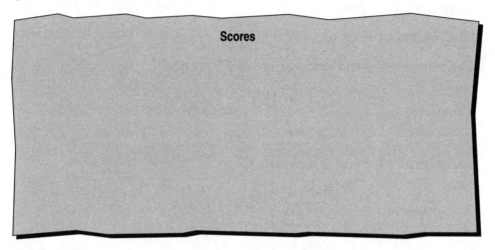

Scores

Tape or copy these scores onto this page. Beside each game create a box for the winning margin. After finding the winning margin for each game, complete the tally chart below.

Winning Margin	Number of Games	Total
1–5 points		
6–10 points		
11–15 points		
16–20 points		
21–25 points		
26 or more points		

After defining a *small winning margin*, write a paragraph supporting your answer to the question of whether most games are decided by a small winning margin.

Try this activity at different times during the season and compare the results.

Average Games

What is the mean, or average, score of a women's college basketball game? Here are the scores of two games.

Louisiana Tech over Tennessee   71 to 68

USC defeated Virginia 85 to 66

The winners scored an average of 78 points.

$$\frac{71 + 85}{2} = 78$$

The average for the losers was 67.

$$\frac{68 + 66}{2} = 67$$

For these two games the average score was 78 to 67.

Here are the scores of six other games.

Seton Hall 64,	Penn State 60
Alabama 73,	Texas Tech 68
Purdue 82,	Texas A&M 56
Stanford 78,	Colorado 62
Connecticut 78,	So. Mississippi 64
North Carolina 73,	Vanderbilt 69

1. What was the average score of these six games?

2. Which do you think is the more realistic average score—the one based on two games or the one based on six games? Why?

More Average Games

What is the mean, or average, score of a basketball game?

First, decide on an approximate number of scores you would need to answer the question. Then, decide on the league you wish to consider. It could be the NBA, or a college, high school, or local league. It could be a men's or women's league. Collect scores from a newspaper or another source. Copy or tape these scores onto this page. Use a calculator to help you find the average score.

Scores

For these _____ games, the average score was _____ .

Repeat this activity at different times of the year or with a different league. Compare the results.

If you have studied mean, median, and mode, investigate which of the three gives the best average score.

Scores to Explore

Collect scores of games from a newspaper to help you explore these questions. Compare your results with those of other students.

- In the NBA, what happens more frequently—each team scores over 100 points in a game or neither team scores 100 points?

- In the NBA, compare the average scores from day to day. See who in the class can find the highest scoring day.

NBA Score Search

Collect the scores for several weeks.

Find a day when . . .

- Every winning team scores over 100 points.

- Two winning teams score the same number of points.

- Over 200 points are scored in every game.

- Two losing teams score the same number of points.

- The winning margins were smallest.

- The home team won every game.

- Write down a "scores" question that you would like to explore.

What's the Score?

A basketball game can be broken down into four quarters or periods.

In the games below use the clues to help you find how many points each team scored in each quarter. To find the final score, add the points scored by each team in each quarter.

					Final Score
Warriors........ 23	30	22	___	___	
Suns .... ___	23	26	32	___	

Clues

- The Suns led by six points at the end of the first quarter.

- In the fourth quarter the Warriors had three fewer points than the Suns.

					Final Score
Hornets 20	25	___	___	___	
Hawks......... 27	26	___	___	___	

Clues

- The fourth quarter was the same as the second quarter.

- 43 points were scored in the third quarter with the Hornets scoring one more point than the Hawks.

					Final Score
Bulls 23	21	___	16	___	
Knicks 24	___	26	___	___	

Clues

- The Bulls led by 2 points at halftime.

- 35 points were scored in the fourth quarter.

- The Bulls had scored 62 points by the end of the third quarter.

					Final Score
Trail Blazers 25	___	___	___	___	
Clippers........ 24	21	___	26	___	

Clues

- In the first half the Trail Blazers scored 54 points.

- The Trail Blazers scored 56 points in the second half—the same number in each of the third and fourth quarters.

- The Clippers scored nine more points in the third quarter than the Trail Blazers did in the first quarter.

To help you understand how basketball summaries work see "How to Read a Quarter-by-Quarter Summary" (page 52).

© Dale Seymour Publications ®

More What's the Score?

Here's a chance for you to create some What's the Score? puzzles. From a newspaper choose a game for which quarter-by-quarter scores are available. Your school coach may be another source for this information.

On a separate piece of paper, write down the quarter-by-quarter points for each team as well as the final score of the game.

On this page, fill in some of the quarter-by-quarter points for the game you selected but leave some of the spaces blank.

List clues that would help a friend complete the quarter-by-quarter points and find the final score.

Give your puzzle to a friend. Did your friend solve the puzzle using your clues?

Teams	1st	Quarter 2d	3d	4th	Final Score

Clues

_____

_____

_____

_____

_____

_____

Choose another game and create a similar puzzle with at least six clues.

For help in reading quarter-by-quarter scores, see "How to Read a Quarter-by-Quarter Summary" (page 52).

A High-Scoring Game

Use these clues to help you find the final score of one of basketball's highest scoring games. Then create a newspaper headline to summarize the game.

Clues

- The Pistons led by four points at the end of the first quarter.

- By halftime, the Nuggets had scored 74 points.

- 76 points were scored in the second quarter.

- The Pistons scored as many points in the third quarter as the Nuggets did in the first quarter.

- After four quarters, the score was 145 to 145.

- 69 points were scored in the fourth quarter.

- In the third overtime period, the Nuggets scored 19 fewer points than they did in the fourth quarter.

- Meanwhile, the Pistons scored 21 fewer points in the third overtime period than they did in the second quarter.

Teams	Quarter				Overtime			Final Score
	1st	2d	3d	4th	1	2	3	
Pistons	38	___	___	___	14	12	___	___
Nuggets	___	___	___	___	14	12	___	___

For help in understanding this quarter-by-quarter scoring summary, see "How to Read a Quarter-by-Quarter Summary" (page 52).

Quarter-by-Quarter Explorations

On this page are the quarter-by-quarter scores for 19 games.

1. Minnesota	17	23	29	30—	99
Atlanta	36	25	33	8—	102
2. New York	19	25	30	28—	102
Cleveland	26	20	29	20—	95
3. Seattle	26	28	17	24—	95
Indiana	31	22	23	25—	101
4. Washington	22	22	21	36—	101
New Jersey	30	34	31	27—	122
5. Orlando	25	27	32	25—	109
Milwaukee	27	23	26	28—	104
6. Dallas	35	23	26	31—	115
Charlotte	31	24	34	21—	110
7. New York	21	23	13	16—	73
Houston	32	17	21	23—	93
8. Boston	33	21	26	32—	112
Miami	25	32	27	20—	104
9. L.A. Lakers	17	20	27	24—	88
Houston	25	23	31	20—	99
10. New Jersey	27	33	34	23—	117
Boston	23	17	27	31—	98

11. Utah	24	13	34	32—	103
L.A. Clippers	28	24	22	25—	99
12. Denver	26	25	22	26—	99
Cleveland	34	30	25	22—	111
13. Portland	22	25	23	24—	94
Indiana	20	28	33	25—	106
14. Portland	28	23	22	33—	106
Dallas	26	23	24	30—	103
15. Denver	22	15	26	21—	84
Golden State	19	26	30	22—	97
16. Utah	23	27	32	21—	103
Phoenix	29	22	26	15—	92
17. Orlando	36	25	25	17—	103
San Antonio	30	24	20	37—	111
18. Chicago	25	24	22	24—	95
Cleveland	30	24	20	25—	99
19. Washington	25	22	34	28—	109
Philadelphia	24	26	21	32—	103

1. Make a guess. In how many of the 19 games do you think the team winning at the end of the first quarter, won the game?

   With the aid of a chart, collect data from the 19 games to check your guess. Express your conclusion in a brief report. Include a graph if this is helpful. Share your report with the class.

2. Explore the question, in how many games did the team trailing at halftime come back to win the game?

For help in reading quarter-by-quarter scores, see "How to Read a Quarter-by-Quarter Summary" (page 52).

More Quarter-by-Quarter Explorations

From a newspaper, cut out the quarter-by-quarter scores of some recent basketball games. Your school basketball coach might be able to give you this information for a local league.

Copy or tape the scores onto this page.

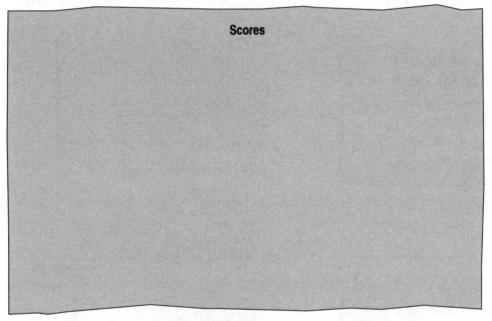

Scores

Here are some possible quarter-by-quarter explorations.

- In how many games did the team leading after the first quarter end up winning the game?

- In how many games did the winning team outscore the losing team in every quarter?

- In how many games did the team trailing at halftime come back to win the game?

- Find a game where a team scored about the same number of points each quarter.

- Brainstorm with your class to find another quarter-by-quarter question to explore.

Choose one of the above explorations. With the aid of a chart, collect data from the games you added to this page. Express your conclusion in a brief report. Include a graph if this is helpful. Share your report with the class.

Hoops Heroes

In basketball each free throw or foul shot is worth one point, baskets or field goals inside the three-point line are worth two points each, and baskets or long field goals beyond the three-point line are worth three points each. Use this information and the newspaper clippings below to learn more about these hoops heroes.

In a recent All Star game, MVP Scottie Pippen had 29 points. This included 5 three-point baskets and 4 two-point baskets.

1. How many foul shots did Pippen make?

Shaquille O'Neal led the Magic with 17 two-point baskets and 15 free throws.

2. How many points did Shaq have?

David Robinson sparked the Spurs with 18 two-point baskets, 13 free throws, and 1 three-point basket.

3. How many points did Robinson have?

The Cavs' Mark Price had 22 points. Price had 2 three-point baskets and 2 foul shots.

4. How many two-point baskets did Price have?

The Suns' Dan Majerle scored 35 points. Majerle had 3 two-point baskets and 5 free throws.

5. How many three-point baskets did Majerle have?

You can create Hoops Heroes questions using of a boxscore.

For example, in the early 1990s, Sheryl Swoopes led Texas Tech in the NCAA women's championship game. From the boxscore for this game comes this information on Swoopes.

> Swoopes 16-24 11-11 47; three-point field goals: 4-6

This line of type contains four facts that interest us.

- the number of successful free throws   11
- the number of three-point field goals   4
- the number of two-point field goals (16 − 4)   12
- total points scored   47

> Since 4 of her 16 field goals were worth 3 points, 12 of them were two-point field goals.

In a Hoop Heroes question, you can use three of these facts and then use arithmetic to find the fourth fact. For example, Sheryl Swoopes had 4 three-point field goals and 12 two-point field goals. She finished the game with 47 points. How many free throws did Swoopes make? $4 \times 3 = 12$; $12 \times 2 = 24$, $12 + 24 = 36$; $47 − 36 = 11$. The answer is 11.

Find a boxscore of a game in which your favorite team was playing.

Record one player's scoring stats.

Player

_____ ____ - ____ ____ - ____ ____ ;

three-point field goals: ____ - ____

Create a Hoops Heroes question based on these stats.

Trade questions with a friend and answer each other's question.

For help in reading a boxscore see "How to Read a Boxscore" (page 53).

Playing the Percentages

A boxscore of a game gives much more detail than just the score. Here is part of a boxscore for a game in which San Antonio scored 107 points.

San Antonio (107)
Rodman 4-6 0-2 8, Ellis 6-11 5-6 20, Robinson 11-21 16-17 39, Anderson 3-11 6-6 12, Knight 1-4 4-5 6, Del Negro 0-0 0-0 0, Cummings 0-1 0-0 0, Reid 4-10 0-0 8, Daniels 4-7 0-0 9, Whitney 2-4 0-0 5. Totals 35-75 31-36 107.

1. Underline Robinson's stats in the boxscore. What was his field goal shooting percent?

2. What was Robinson's foul shot shooting percent?

3. Which players had a field goal shooting percent over 50%?

4. Which player had the highest field goal shooting percent?

5. Which player had the highest foul shot shooting percent?

For help in reading this boxscore and in answering the questions, see "How to Read a Boxscore" (page 53).

More Playing the Percentages

From a newspaper or other sources, choose a boxscore of a game in which one of your favorite teams was playing.

The game could be from men's or women's basketball. It could be an elementary school, high school, college, or professional game.

Attach the boxscore to this page.

Choose one of the players in the boxscore. Underline or highlight this player's stats.

1. What was this player's field goal shooting percent?

2. What was this player's foul shot shooting percent?

Choose one of the two teams. On this team . . .

3. Which players had a field goal shooting percent over 50%?

4. Which player had the highest field goal shooting percent?

5. Which player had the highest foul shot shooting percent?

6. Using the data from the boxscore, create your own question. Give it to a friend to answer.

7. Collect more boxscores and follow your favorite players for a week or more. Calculate their field goal and foul shot shooting percents each game.

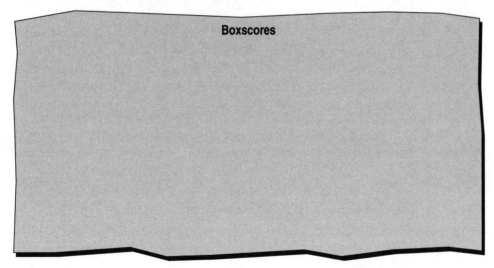

Boxscores

For help in reading a boxscore, see "How to Read a Boxscore" (page 53).

Scouting Report

It will help to work as a group with a few other students for this investigation. You will need at least 10 boxscores of games involving either your favorite team or any other collection of 10 boxscores. A newspaper is a good source for this data.

Which of the following statements is most likely to be true?

A. The team with the better field goal shooting percent wins.

B. The team with the better free throw shooting percent wins.

C. The team with the better three-point field goal shooting percent wins.

Working cooperatively, check the accuracy of your guess by recording data from the 10 boxscores you collected. Write a brief report in which you state your conclusion and the reason your group reached that conclusion. You can then check your results with an even larger collection of boxscores.

Working in a small group, study the boxscores to find other keys to being a winning team. Share your findings with the class.

To learn to read a boxscore, see "How to Read a Boxscore" (page 53).

Choose a date in the season when your favorite team will be playing. Make a guess as to which three players will score the most points in that game. Record their names below. After the game,

1. Fill in how many three-point field goals, two-point field goals, and foul shots each player actually made.

2. Calculate each player's points.

3. Add up each player's points to find your total.

Compare your total with that of a friend. Who was the better coach?

| Player | Number of | | | |
	Three-Point Field Goals	Two-Point Field Goals	Free Throws	Points
Total				

How to Read a Quarter-by-Quarter Summary

A basketball game can be broken down into four quarters or periods. This is a quarter-by-quarter breakdown of the scoring in a recent Spurs/Pistons game.

	Quarter				Final
	1st	2d	3d	4th	Score
Pistons	20	27	21	28	96
Spurs	22	28	31	34	115

In the game, the Spurs scored 22 + 28 + 31+ 34 = 115 points.

The Pistons scored 20 points in the first quarter.

By halftime the Spurs had scored 22 + 28 = 50 points.

In the third quarter 21 + 31 = 52 points were scored.

By the end of the third quarter, the Pistons had scored 20 + 27 + 21 = 68 points.

In the newspaper the quarter-by-quarter summary for this game would appear like this.

Pistons	20	27	21	28— 96
Spurs	22	28	31	34—115

How to Read a Boxscore

In basketball each successful free throw or foul shot is worth 1 point, field goals or baskets from shots taken inside the three-point line are worth 2 points each, while baskets or long field goals on shots taken beyond the three-point line are worth 3 points each.

This is part of a boxscore.

Shaquille O'Neal was successful on 10 out of 16 field goal shots. He also was successful on 3 out of the 9 foul shots. He scored 23 points.

Orlando 103 at Portland 88

Orlando (103)

Anderson 3-6 0-0 9, Turner 5-12 0-0 10, O'Neal 10-16 3-9 23, Hardaway 5-13 1-2 12, Skiles 8-16 3-4 22, Scott 8-16 4-4 22, Kite 0-2 0-0 0, Royal 1-3 3-4 5, L. Williams 0-0 0-0 0, Green 0-2 0-0 0, Lichti 0-0 0-0 0, Bowie 0-1 0-0 0. Totals 40-87 14-23 103.

Three-point goals—Orlando 9-18 (Anderson 3-5, Skiles 3-5, Scott 2-4, Hardaway 1-3, Turner 0-1).

Orlando made 40 out of 87 field goal shots, along with 14 out of 23 foul shots. They scored 103 points.

- Anfernee Hardaway's shooting percents were

  Field goals $\frac{5}{13} = 38\%$

  Foul shots $\frac{1}{2} = 50\%$

  Three-point field goals $\frac{1}{3} = 33\%$

- Orlando's field goal shooting percent was $\frac{40}{87} = 46\%$.

- Orlando's foul shooting was $\frac{14}{23} = 61\%$.

- In three-point shots Orlando was $\frac{9}{18} = 50\%$.

SECTION 4
• •

Hockey

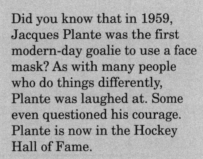

On December 11, 1985, the
Blackhawks scored 9 goals,
three fewer than the Oilers.
What was the score of the
game?

Did you know that the new
arena in Boston has a main
ramp inclined at 13 degrees?
This is because circus
elephants won't climb a ramp
any steeper.

Did you know that in 1959,
Jacques Plante was the first
modern-day goalie to use a face
mask? As with many people
who do things differently,
Plante was laughed at. Some
even questioned his courage.
Plante is now in the Hockey
Hall of Fame.

Did you know that Bill
Mosienko once scored 3 goals
in just 21 seconds?

Are these still records?

• Wayne Gretzky—92 goals
  in one season

• Wayne Gretzky—163
  assists in one season

• Wayne Gretzky—215
  points in one season

• Wayne Gretzky—scored at
  least a point a game for 51
  games in a row

No wonder he is called "The
Great Gretzky."

Did you know that on
February 7, 1976, Darryl
Sittler scored 6 goals and had
4 assists?

Checkerboard Scores

The chart below summarizes the scores of 100 National Hockey League (NHL) games. Legends on the left and on the bottom tell the losing and winning team scores. The body of the table tells the numbers of the games in which each score was made.

Three games ended in a 2 to 2 tie.

In six games the score was 5 to 4.

**Frequency of Scores
100 NHL Games**

Goals by losing team

	0	1	2	3	4	5	6	7	8
6							0	1	0
5						2	2	0	0
4					0	6	0	2	0
3				2	14	5	8	1	1
2			3	8	6	8	1	0	1
1		2	8	4	6	1	1	0	1
0	0	0	0	2	2	0	1	0	1

Goals by winning team

1. What was the most frequent score?

2. What percent of games ended in a tie?

3. In what percent of games was the winning margin three goals? This means games with scores 3 to 0, 4 to 1, 5 to 2, 6 to 3, 7 to 4, or 8 to 5.

4. What was the most frequent winning margin—one goal, two goals, or three goals?

5. What was the most frequent total of goals scored by both teams in a game?

More Checkerboard Scores

Using the newspaper as a source, collect scores of hockey games. The more scores you collect, the more interesting the results will be. Record the frequency of each score in the grid below. Then answer the questions.

Instead of using the grid, you could use a checkerboard. For each game of a certain score, add a checker to the appropriate square. Visually this makes a nice three-dimensional graph.

Frequency of Scores

	0	1	2	3	4	5	6	7	8
6									
5									
4									
3									
2									
1									
0									

Goals by losing team (vertical axis)

Goals by winning team (horizontal axis)

1. What was the most frequent score?

2. What percent of games ended in a tie?

3. In what percent of games was the winning margin three goals?

4. What was the most frequent winning margin—one goal, two goals, or three goals?

5. What was the most frequent total of goals scored by both teams in a game?

Closing the Gap

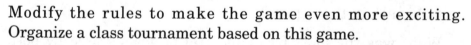

To determine the individual scoring leaders, a player receives one point for each goal and also one point for each assist.

This leads to the formula

$$\text{goals (G)} + \text{assist (A)} = \text{points (P)}.$$

Using addition or subtraction, complete this Scoring Leaders list from a newspaper.

	G	A	P
Federov	14	15	29
Jagr	8	—	28
Bure	—	12	26
Leetch	12	14	—

Clip out a Scoring Leaders column from the newspaper. Copy some of your favorite players' G, A, P stats on the blackboard, but leave one of the three numbers blank. Have the class fill in the blank using addition or subtraction.

The Gap Game

Look for the Scoring Leaders column in the newspaper. On a separate file card for each player, copy the first 10 players' names along with their goals, assists, and points.

After shuffling the 10 cards, deal 5 to a friend and keep 5 yourself. Add up the number of goals your five players have scored. Do the same for the number of assists and the number of points. Compare your three answers with your friend's answers. The winner of the hand is the one who wins at least two out of the three categories. Reshuffle the cards and play again.

Modify the rules to make the game even more exciting. Organize a class tournament based on this game.

These activities could also be done using school, local, or minor league statistics.

Talent Scout

To play Talent Scout, divide your class into small groups. Each group picks a group name and a hockey team. Select the names of five players from the team.

For that team's next two games, record the number of goals, assists, and points made by each of your players. (This information will be in game scoring summaries found in the newspaper after a game.)

Which group in the class had the most points?

An interesting variation is to select players from any team, choosing more than five players, and to consider more than two games.

Team Name:			
Players	Goals	Assists	Points
Total			

If you need help see "How to Read a Game Scoring Summary" (page 65).

Puzzlers

To solve these puzzles you need follow only two rules.

- For the team, every game played is either a win or a loss or a tie.

- Each win is worth 2 points, each tie is worth 1 point, and each loss is worth 0 points.

Solve these puzzles; fill in the blanks.

	GP	W	L	T	Pts
San Jose	___	11	16	5	___
Anaheim	31	___	19	2	___
Toronto	34	20	7	___	___
New Jersey	___	___	9	4	38
Pittsburgh	___	15	8	___	37
Florida	30	___	14	___	28

If you do not understand the information, see "How to Read the Team Standings" (page 64).

From the newspaper, clip out the hockey standings of a league that interests you. Choose a team from that league's standings. Then choose one of the six puzzle formats and circle the one you have chosen.

Puzzle Formats

	GP	W	L	T	Pts
Puzzle 1	?	X	X	X	X
Puzzle 2	?	X	X	X	?
Puzzle 3	X	?	X	X	?
Puzzle 4	?	?	X	X	X
Puzzle 5	X	X	?	?	X
Puzzle 6	X	?	X	?	X

To create a puzzle, combine the statistics of your chosen team with the puzzle format you selected. Wherever there is an X in your chosen format, fill in Your Puzzle with the numbers from your team. Wherever there is a ? in the format, put a ? in your puzzle.

Your Puzzle

Team	GP	W	L	T	Pts
_____	_____	_____	_____	_____	_____

Tear off below the dotted line and have a friend try to figure out what numbers the question marks represent.

Become an expert at solving all six puzzle formats.

Invent another puzzle format.

If you are not sure how to read the standings see "How to Read the Team Standings" (page 64).

How Well Do You Know Hockey?

Circle the percent of games for which you think the statement is true.

Approximate Percent of Games

1. The home team wins.   less than 50%   50%   66%   75%   more than 85%

2. The team that scores first, wins.   less than 50%   50%   66%   75%   more than 85%

3. When the home team scores first, it wins.   less than 50%   50%   66%   75%   more than 85%

4. The team that is winning at the end of the first period wins the game.   less than 50%   50%   66%   75%   more than 85%

5. The team with the more shots on goal wins the game.   less than 50%   50%   66%   75%   more than 85%

6. The team with the better power-play percent wins the game.   less than 50%   50%   66%   75%   more than 85%

7. Overtime games end in a tie.   less than 50%   50%   66%   75%   more than 85%

To check the accuracy of your answers, collect game scoring summaries from the newspaper for at least 20 games.

Each small group could check out the statistics for one of the above statements and report to the rest of the class.

Would these results hold true if you only considered your favorite team? Check it out.

What other questions could you investigate using the game scoring summaries?

For help in reading the summaries in the newspaper, see "How to Read a Game Scoring Summary" (page 65).

Goals against average is the most common statistic used to compare goalies in hockey.

Goals against average is found using this formula.

$$\text{Avg} = \frac{60 \times \text{Goals Allowed}}{\text{Minutes Played}}$$

For example, partway through a season Dominic Hasek had allowed 30 goals in 976 minutes of play.

His goals against average was $\dfrac{60 \times 30}{976} = 1.84$

This means that Hasek allowed an average of less than two goals per game.

• Using game scoring summaries from the newspaper, follow your favorite goalie for a number of games, then calculate his goals against average. The smaller the goals against average, the better the goalie.

Another statistic used to compare goalies is the save average. The save average formula is

$$\text{Save Avg} = \frac{\text{Shots Stopped}}{\text{Shots Attempted}}$$

For example, if goalie Felix Potvin allowed two goals, and his opponents had 32 shots on goal, then Potvin's save average

would be $\dfrac{30}{32} = .937$

• Consider all the game scoring summaries in the newspaper on one day. Find the goalie with the highest (best) save average.

• Which do you think is the better indicator of a good goalie— goals against average or save average? Make a presentation, using statistics, to convince your classmates.

If you are not sure see "How to Read a Game Scoring Summary" (page 65).

How to Read the Team Standings

In the newspaper, you will find the team standings for a variety of hockey leagues. The most detailed standings contain this information.

GP or G   games played
W   wins
L   losses
T   tie games
Pts or P   points—A team receives 2 points for each win, 1 point for each tie, and 0 points for each loss.
GF   goals for: the number of goals scored by the team all season
GA   goals against: the number of goals scored against the team all season
LAST 10   W-L-T of the team's last 10 games
HOME   W-L-T of the team's home games over the season
AWAY   W-L-T of the team's games away from home over the season

The team with the most points is in first place; the team with the fewest points is in last place.

How to Read a Game Scoring Summary

These examples will help you understand the shorthand used in a game scoring summary found in a newspaper.

- The visiting team is always "at" the home team.

- A hockey game is divided into three 20-minute periods. In the National Hockey League, if a game is tied after the three periods, it goes into overtime. The first team to score in overtime wins the game. If nobody scores within five minutes, then the game is stopped and is called a tie.

- Here is an example of how a goal is reported.

> 1 Vancouver, Bure 31 (Linden) 7:47

This means that the first goal of the game was scored by Vancouver's Pavel Bure after 7 minutes and 47 seconds of play in the period. It was Bure's 31st goal of the season. Trevor Linden received an assist on the goal.

- Here is an example of how shots on goal are reported:

> **Shots on goal**—Chicago 6-11-10—27

This means that Chicago had 6 shots on goal in the first period, 11 in the second period, and 10 in the third period for a total of 27 shots during the game.

- A team has a power play chance when it has more players on the ice than its opponents. This happens when the opposition receives a penalty.

Power plays are reported as:

> **Power-play opportunities**   Los Angeles 1 of 4

This means that Los Angeles had four different power play opportunities and scored a goal on one of them. This statistic can also be expressed as a success rate of $\frac{1}{4}$ or 0.25 or 25%.

SECTION 5

Other Sports

Evan Williams can drive a golf ball through a one-inch-thick telephone book. The ball then travels another 150 yards. How big a city would you need to have a one-inch-thick telephone book. What letter of the alphabet would be at one inch into the New York City telephone book?

Prime Time Wrestling

Weight (pounds)
Mr. Perfect. 291
Crush. 293
Doink. 258
Hulk Hogan 303
Randy Savage. 242
Bret Hart 274

Consider these to be actual wrestlers' weights and wrestle this problem to the ground. When two wrestlers meet, the heavier wrestler wins, unless the difference of their weights is a prime number. Which one of the wrestlers can beat all the others?

Marathon Soaking

British businessman Tom Granby found he'd dived off the high board after he agreed to sponsor a young girl in a charity swim at the rate of $6 for every length of the pool she completed.

He expected to have to pay out around $100.

But he didn't know the girl was a marathon swimmer. She swam 1,214 lengths, and now Granby has received a reminder that his pledge amounts to something over $7,000. He's refusing to pay.

The London newspaper columnist John Junor said, "I back him in the refusal. There are times when charity demands come perilously close to moral blackmail. And this is one of them."

Do you think that Tom should have to pay?

Here are the results of a survey showing the number of Canadians participating in various sports.

Swimming 6,103,943
Water Skiing 1,002,478
Windsurfing 375,124
Lawn Bowling 29,386

As a sixteen-year-old from Placentia, California, Janet Evans won three gold medals in the 1988 Olympic Games. In the 1992 Olympics, she won the women's 800-meter swimming event and became the first woman to win gold medals in that event two Olympics in a row. After winning in 1992, Evans said, "Four years is a long time to dedicate yourself to swimming four hours a day . . . and that makes this even more sweet."

Below are the results of the 1992 race.

1992 Olympic Women's 800-Meter Freestyle

Position	Name	Time
1	Janet Evans	8:25.52
2	Hayley Lewis	8:30.34
3	Jana Henke	8:30.99
4	Philippa Langrel	8:35.57
5	Irene Dalby	8:37.12
6	Olga Splichalova	8:37.66
7	Erika Hansen	8:39.25
8	Isabelle Arnould	8:41.86

8 minutes, 25.52 seconds

1. Who won the race?

2. What was the winner's time?

3. By how much did she win?

4. Which two swimmers were closest? How close?

5. Which two swimmers were just one position apart, but the most time apart?

Another activity is to write each swimmer's name and time on a separate file card. After shuffling the cards distribute one card to each student. The students should then line up from first to last.

Look for some swimming race results in a newspaper. Another source may be a high school or swim club coach. Copy the information below and then answer the questions.

Race Results

Name	Time
_____	_____
_____	_____
_____	_____
_____	_____
_____	_____
_____	_____
_____	_____
_____	_____

1. Who won the race?

2. What was the winner's time?

3. By how much did the first place swimmer win?

4. How many swimmers were within one second of winning?

5. Which two swimmers were closest? How close?

6. Which two swimmers were just one position apart, but the most time apart?

More Activities

• Write each swimmer's name and time on a separate file card. After shuffling the cards, distribute the one card to a student. The students should then line up from first to last.

• Collect results from the freestyle, butterfly, backstroke, and breaststroke events. Use these results to help you convince the class which stroke is the most difficult.

Which Country Did the Best?

Whenever there is international competition, the question arises as to which country did the best. For example, below are the first 16 finishers in the 1994 Winter Olympic women's downhill skiing race. The skiers came from 10 different countries.

> **1994 Winter Olympics Women's Downhill Skiing**
> 1. Katja Seizinger, Germany, 1 minute, 35.93 seconds; 2. Picabo Street, USA, 1:36.59; 3. Isolde Kostner, Italy, 1:36.85; 4. Martina Ertl, Germany, 1:37.10; 5. Catherine Pace, Canada, 1:37.17; 6. Melanie Suchet, France, 1:37.34; 7. Hilary Lindh, USA, 1:37.44; 8. Varvara Zelenskaia, Russia, 1:37.48; 9. Pernilla Wiberg, Sweden, 1:37.61; 10. Katja Koren, Slovenia, 1:37.69; 11. Jeanette Lunde, Norway, 1:37.80; 12. Miriam Vogt, Germany, 1:37.86; 13. Florence Masnada, France, 1:37.92; 14. Morena Gallizio, Italy, 1:37.94; 15. Veronika Stallmaier, Austria, 1:37.94. 16. Alenka Dovzan, Slovenia, 1:38.07.

1. Who won the race? What was her time? What was her country?

2. Based on this race, which country did the best?

Use cooperative learning to help you answer the question. Divide the class into small groups. Each group is to devise a system to decide which country did the best in this competition.

Report your group's system to the rest of the class. Is it reasonable for the groups to have different answers? As a class, evaluate the strengths and weaknesses of each group's system.

More Which Country Did the Best?

Many sports are decided by time, such as downhill skiing, speed skating, swimming, track, and marathon races. Can you think of any others? Choose an international sport for which you can get a list of individual times from a newspaper. Attach this list to the page.

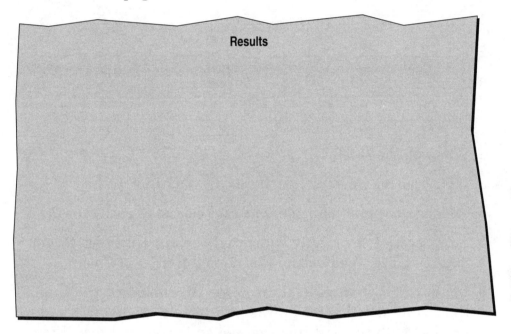

Results

Based on this race, which country did the best?

Use cooperative learning to help you answer the question. Divide the class into small groups. Each group is to devise a system to decide which country did the best in the competition.

Report your group's system to the rest of the class. Is it reasonable for the groups to have different answers? As a class, evaluate the strengths and weaknesses of each group's system.

What other sports would fit into this category? Investigate one of these sports to decide which country did the best.

How do sports like ski jumping or discus throwing differ from the sports listed above?

In this investigation the word *country* could be replaced by *high school* or *college*. Use this investigation to compare the performance of several schools in a timed individual event.

On Track

Ubeja Anderson 10.54

Leroy Burrell 10.27

Patrick Delice 10.70

Jon Drummond 10.42

Robert Esmie 10.53

Sam Jefferson 10.58

Henry Neal 10.60

Jeff Williams 10.56

Here are the results of the 100-meter dash at a track meet in New York.

1. Complete the order of finish.

Name	Time		Name	Time
1 _____	_____	5	_____	_____
2 _____	_____	6	_____	_____
3 _____	_____	7	_____	_____
4 _____	_____	8	_____	_____

2. Who won the race?

3. What was his time?

4. Which two runners finished the race closest to each other?

5. Suppose the clock only indicated the time correct to one decimal place. What would this do to the order of finish?

6. In the 1992 Olympics, there were 16 women in the semi-final, 400-meter race. It was run in two heats. The eight runners with the best times moved on to the final race. From the results of the two heats, write down the eight women who went on to the final race.

Heat 1:
Olga, Bryzgina 49.76
Ximena Gaviria 49.76
Natasha Kaiser 50.60
Michelle Lock 50.78
Jearl Miles 50.57
Marie Josee Perec 49.48
Yelena Ruzina 51.30
Phyllis Smith 50.40

Heat 2:
Norfalia Carabali 51.75
Elsa Devassoigne 52.85
Sandra Douglas 51.96
Olga Nazarova 50.31
Renee Poetschka 52.09
Sandie Richards 50.35
Jill Richardson-Briscoe 50.02
Rochelle Stevens 50.37

Name	Time		Name	Time
1 _____	_____	5	_____	_____
2 _____	_____	6	_____	_____
3 _____	_____	7	_____	_____
4 _____	_____	8	_____	_____

7. How far away from qualifying for the final race was the 9th best runner in the semifinals?

8. Guess who won gold, silver, and bronze in the final race.

More on Track

From a newspaper, select the results from one of your favorite events in any track meet. Create three questions for the class to answer from these results.

There are many ideas for questions on other blackline masters such as, "On Track," "Which Country Did the Best?," "On the Run," and "Olympic Gold."

However don't hesitate to use your ideas.

1. _____

   _____

2. _____

   _____

3. _____

   _____

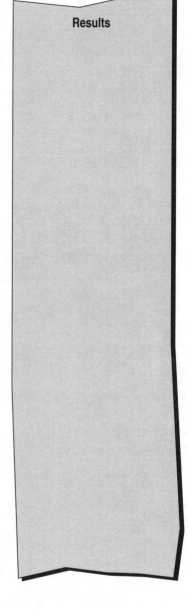

Results

One of the world's all-time great athletes is Jackie Joyner-Kersee. When Jackie Joyner-Kersee was born, she was named after Jacqueline Kennedy, the wife of the President of the United States. Her mother felt she would "be the First Lady of something." She certainly was. Bruce Jenner called her "the best athlete ever."

Jackie Joyner-Kersee won an Olympic gold medal in the long jump and two Olympic gold medals in the heptathlon. The heptathlon takes place over two days. The first day, four events take place—100-meter hurdles, high jump, shot put, and 200-meter race. Day two has the long jump, javelin, and the 800-meter race. It is the ultimate challenge of the Olympic motto—higher, stronger, faster.

Which of the heptathlon events are based on time and which are based on distance? The latter are called field events.

Look for field events results in the newspaper and create some questions for your classmates to enjoy.

Which Is the Fastest Sport?

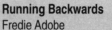

Running Backwards Fredie Adobe 100 yards 12.7 sec	**Downhill Skiing** Tommy Moe 9600 feet 1 min 45.75 sec
Skateboarding Roger Hickey 3 miles 3 min 15 sec	**Cycling** Greg Lemond 2390 miles 87 hr, 38 min, 35 sec
Swimming Jenny Thompson 100 yards 47.74 sec	**Speed Skating** Bonnie Blair 1000 meters 1 min 18.74 sec
Luge Cammy Myler 3280 feet 49.201 sec	**Snowshoeing** Jeremy Badeau 100 meters 14.02 sec

Based on the above statistics, rank the sports from fastest (1) to slowest (8). Use as much estimation and comparison as you can. Do as little arithmetic as possible.

Which sports go above the speed limit?

Is this a reasonable way to compare the speed of sports?

In 1897, the first Boston Marathon was held; only fifteen ran. By the 1990s, over 9000 participated each year. In the 1950s winning times improved dramatically. Only later was it discovered that the course had become 913 yards short of the 26 miles, 385 yards. The shortage occurred because of road construction in the Boston suburbs.

Here are the top five finishers in 1994 for both men and women. Uta Pippig had a time of 2 hours, 21 minutes, and 45 seconds.

Men
1 Cosmas Ndeti 2:07:15
2 Andres Espinosa 2:07:19
3 Jackson Kipngok 2:08:08
4 Young-Jo Hwang 2:08:09
5 Arturo Barrios. 2:08:28

Women
1 Uta Pippig 2:21:45
2 Valentina Yegorova 2:23:33
3 Elana Meyer. 2:25:15
4 Alena Peterkova 2:25:19
5 Carmen De Oliveira 2:27:41

1. By how much did Ndeti win?

2. By how much did Pippig win over the next fastest woman?

3. How much difference was there between the fifth-place finisher and the winner in both the women's and men's categories?

4. Which two men were closest? Which two women were closest?

5. On the average, how many miles per hour was Cosmas Ndeti traveling?

6. Explain this graph to a friend. Over the 26 miles what would be the most difficult part of the race? Why?

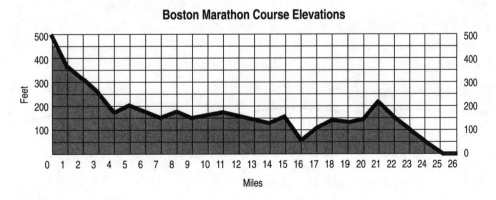

Boston Marathon Course Elevations

Many cities host road races during the year. Look for their results in the newspaper. Make up some questions to go with these results.

Figure Skating Figures

Figure skating is a two day event. The first day is the technical program. The second day is the free skating.

Each day, the judges rank the skaters first, second, third, and so forth on that day's skating. Then this formula is used.

$$\text{Placement Points} = \frac{\text{Technical Ranking}}{2} + \text{Free-Skating Ranking}$$

(To check your understanding of this formula see Katarina Witt's rankings below.)

At the end of the two days, the lower the placement points the higher the finish!

Below are the first and second days' rankings from the Women's Singles Figure Skating at the 1994 Olympics.

1994 Winter Olympics Women's Singles Figure Skating				
Name	Technical Ranking	Free-Skating Ranking	Placement Points	Order of Finish
Nancy Kerrigan	1	2	_____	_____
Oksana Baiul	2	1	_____	_____
Surya Bonaly	3	4	_____	_____
Chen Lu	4	3	_____	_____
Tanja Szewczenko	5	6	_____	_____
Katarina Witt	6	8	11.0	_____
Yuka Sato	7	5	_____	_____
Josee Chouinard	8	9	_____	_____
Anna Rechnio	9	12	_____	_____
Tonya Harding	10	7	_____	_____

1. Complete the missing placement points, and then rank the skaters' order of finish from first to tenth.

2. Let's pretend. Let the technical ranking of the skaters remain the same. Assume each skater is in the top ten in free skating. Make up a new ranking in the free skating that would enable Tonya Harding to have a third-place finish. Compare your answer with a friend's.

More Figure Skating Figures

"If anyone can do it, Kurt can. But it will come down to mathematics in the end." These words were spoken by Brian Boitano after skater Kurt Browning had had a disappointing first-day performance. In Figure Skating Figures, we learned the mathematics that Boitano was talking about.

In the newspaper look for the technical and free-skating rankings in a skating competition.

Fill in the chart below leaving the right hand two columns blank.

Name	Technical Ranking	Free Skating Ranking	Placement Points	Order of Finish

1. Complete the missing placement points and then rank the skaters' order of finish from first to tenth.

2. Let's pretend. Let the technical ranking of the skaters remain the same. Suppose each skater is in the top ten in free skating. Make up a new ranking in the free skating which would enable your favorite skater to improve. Compare your answer with a friend's.

World Cup Soccer

World Cup 1994, which was held in the USA, was a tremendous success. Over 3.5 million people attended the games and one out of every four people around the world watched on television as Brazil beat Italy in the championship game.

The United States's team was also successful as it advanced beyond the first round. For its first three games, the United States was in Group A.

The Group A scores were USA 2, Columbia 1; USA 1, Switzerland 1; Romania 1, USA 0; Romania 3, Columbia 1; Switzerland 4, Romania 1; Columbia 2, Switzerland 0

1. Use these scores to complete the standings.

Team	W	L	T	GF	GA
Romania	___	___	___	___	___
Switzerland	___	___	___	___	___
USA	___	___	___	___	___
Columbia	___	___	___	___	___

wins → *losses* → *ties* goals for (goals scored by the team) goals against

Use logic and the standings to help you find the missing scores below.

2. In 1982, Italy won the World Cup even though it didn't win one game in the first round.

Country	W	L	T	GF	GA
Poland	1	0	2	5	1
Italy	0	0	3	2	2
Cameroon	0	0	3	1	1
Peru	0	1	2	2	6

Poland 5, Peru 1

Poland _____ , Italy _____

Poland _____ , Cameroon _____

Italy _____ , Cameroon _____

Italy _____ , Peru _____

Cameroon _____ , Peru _____

3. In 1986, Poland scored only one goal but still advanced into the next round.

Country	W	L	T	GF	GA
Morocco	1	0	2	3	1
England	1	1	1	3	1
Poland	1	1	1	1	3
Portugal	1	2	0	2	4

England 3, Poland 0

England _____ , Morocco _____

England _____ , Portugal _____

Morocco _____ , Poland _____

Morocco _____ , Portugal _____

Poland _____ , Portugal _____

The game is played on a field of graph paper (32 by 20 squares).

One player takes the ball at the center of the field, then the players continue in alternate moves.

Each move consists of drawing three line segments along either the diagonals or the sides of the grid squares. In this way the players alternately move the ball to another grid point.

Rules of Play

1. The edge of the field may not be touched or crossed.

2. The zigzag line formed during previous play may not be touched or crossed.

The only exception to Rule 1 is that the goal line between the goalposts may be touched or crossed, which counts as a goal.

The game ends when a goal is scored.

There is also an exception to Rule 2. Player A may be able to maneuver Player B into a position so that Player B can not make a move. In that case Player A moves again. This second move must be six lines long. It may also cross a previous line of play.

Study the game below and then set up your own grid. The solid lines shows the moves of the starting player, the dotted lines are the moves of the second player.

Challenge a friend to a game. See who in the class is interested in playing in a tournament. One loss and you're out!

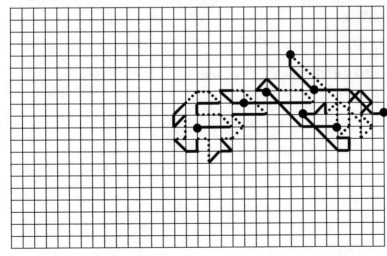

Fore

On February 9, 1980, Lang Martin balanced 7 golf balls vertically.

Nick Price sank a 110-foot putt in the 1992 PGA Championship.

Thad Daber shot a 70 using only a 6-iron.

Arthur Thompson is the oldest person to shoot his age—103.

In Bermuda, Joe Flynn shot an 82 by throwing his golf ball around the course.

Mental Math

To find a total golf score for four rounds, it's easier to think "under par" and "over par" than to add up the four scores. For example, on a par 71 course, Patty Sheehan shot 66-71-69-71 over the four days. To find her total score it's easier to think 5 under par, par, 2 under par, and par for a total of 7 under par for the four rounds. Since par for the four rounds is 284, Sheehan shot 284 − 7 = 277.

In another tournament, Hollis Stacey shot 73-73-71-68. On the par-72 course, par for the tournament was 4×72 or 288 shots. Stacey was one over par, one over par, one under par, and four under par. Therefore, for the tournamaent, Stacey was three under par. She took 288 − 3 = 285 shots.

Look up some tournament results in the newspaper and practice your mental math.

Some Different Sports

Occasionally there is news of some unusual sporting event. Have you ever heard of the cow-chip toss? You will see other examples of throwing achievements as you try the test.

To help you out, you can work with a small group to decide which answer in brackets goes in each blank. Good luck.

Judy Horowitz threw a frisbee ____ feet and caught it herself before the frisbee landed. This happened June 29, 1985, at La Mirada, California.

At the Iowa State Fair on August 21, 1979, Lori Adams hurled a two-pound rolling pin ____ feet.

On September 6, 1981, two Finnish men threw a fresh egg ____ feet without the egg breaking.

In Boston on May 27, 1991, James Deady threw a grape ____ feet to Paul Travilla. Paul caught the grape in his mouth.

In England on July 19, 1978, Geoff Capes threw a five-pound brick ____ feet.

Beaver, Okla. —Leland Searcy, the world record holder in the cow-chip toss, showed he's still the best in his field.

On Saturday, Searcy threw one of the dried manure discs over 54 meters to beat 24 challengers and win the eighth annual World Championship Cow Chip Contest.

The Beaver resident, who competes in the men's open division, set the world record in 1979 with a toss of over 55 meters.

"It was perfect cow-chip throwing weather," said Nancy Calhoon, executive director of the Beaver Chamber of Commerce.

"There was very little wind and it was about seventy degrees. It was just right."

[Answers: 146, 175, 197, 317, 328]

Give your group one point for every correct answer. What was your score out of five? Unfortunately one mistake can affect all your answers.

If you are disappointed in your score then try to devise a scoring system that would reward groups for being close to having the right answers. Share your scoring system with the class. Do you think any of the above events are real sports? Debate this.

The Amazing Ashrita

Ashrita Furman is super fit. Just look at the list of things he has done. The health food store manager from Brooklyn, New York, admits he may "be a little eccentric, but not crazy." Furman says that in school he was "totally unathletic."

Why the change? Well, Furman believes in the concept of mental determination. He also feels that there is a tremendous power within each individual. His most difficult accomplishment? Somersaulting over 12 miles.

Ashrita's Accomplishments

Hand clapping, 50 hours, NYC, 1981

Jumping jacks, 33,000, NYC, 1982

Somersaults, distance, 12 miles, 390 yards, Lexington to Charlestown, Mass., 1986

Aqua pogo (underwater), 3 hours, 20 minutes, NYC, 1986

Aqua pogo, 3 hours, 40 minutes, Amazon River, Peru, 1987

Skip running, 10 miles (1 hour, 15 minutes, 33 seconds), Zurich, Switzerland, 1987

Continuous juggling, 6 hours, 7 minutes, NYC, 1987

Pogo juggling, 1 hour, 1 minute, Orlando, 1988

Joggling, fastest marathon (juggling while running), 26.2 miles in 3 hours, 22 minutes, Salmon River, Idaho, 1988

Joggling, longest distance, 50 miles in 8 hours, 52 minutes, NYC, 1989

Milk bottle balancing, 43.75 miles, NYC, 1990

Hopscotch, 307 games in 24 hours, Zurich, Switzerland, 1991

Pogo stick (distance), 14.99 miles, Seoul, Korea, 1991

Burpees (squat thrusts), 1,649 in 1 hour, NYC, 1992

Milk bottle balancing, 61 miles, NYC, 1992

Squats, 3,038 in 1 hour, a hot-air balloon in Post Mills, Vt., 1992

Squats, 3,913 in 1 hour, Dumaguete, Philippines, 1993

- From the list, which feat do you think would be the most difficult to do?

- Make a graph of your class' answers to this question.

- Look for other fantastic athletic feats in the newspaper.

Want to Trade Cards?

Is there anybody in your class who has sports cards? Some of these cards are very valuable. There is an old Honus Wagner card worth hundreds of thousands of dollars.

Many sports have cards—the most popular are baseball, football, hockey, and basketball.

Bring your sports cards to class.

Most of the cards show a player's uniform number. You can use these numbers to make some interesting human equations. For example,

$$\text{Griffey} + \text{Olerud} = \text{Avery}$$

$$24 + 9 = 33$$

- Use your cards to create three more human equations.

- Create a human equation using a different operation.

- Create a human equation with more than three players.

What other sources are there for player numbers? Use one of those sources for interesting human equations.

- Try the human equation activity by assigning uniform numbers to each member of your class.

- Since most cards contain the athlete's birthday, activities can be designed based on the blackline master "Happy Birthday."

- After studying your cards, design your own sports cards activities.

Happy Birthday

For these activities, you will need a roster or list of birth dates of players on a team—local, school, or professional. Magazines, game programs, and sometimes newspapers, or a coach or teacher may have this information. Another good source is sports cards. You could also try these activities using your classmates' birth dates.

- Who is the oldest player?

- How old is he or she?

- Who is the youngest player?

- How old is he or she?

- How old is your favorite player?

- Which players celebrate a birthday closest together?

- Do any players have the same birthday?

- Write down the month and day of your birth. Which player has a birthday closest to your birthday?

- Make a graph to show how many players were born in each month.

Did you know that in a group of 23 people there is a fifty-fifty chance that at least two people have the same birthday? This is shown on the graph below. Test this with your class or team. What other information can you learn from this graph?

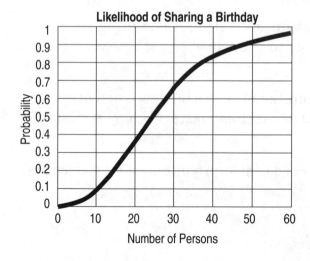

SECTION 6
Language

Headliners

Headline Hunters

From a newspaper choose a main story of a recent game. Cut off the headline, leaving only the story. Have a friend read the story and then create a new headline for the story. Compare your friend's headline with the one from the newspaper. What characteristics does a good headline have?

Making Headlines

In the newspaper, look for a headline from a recent game. Cut out the headline and then cut the headline into separate words. Mix up the words before giving them to a friend. Can your friend rearrange the words into a headline? Is there more than one headline that makes sense using these words?

Keep Your Balance

The sports pages are made up of pictures, statistics, and text. Which do you think takes up the most space? Compare your estimate with others.

Discuss ways to determine what takes up the most space. Test your ideas. Was your estimate correct? Would your conclusion be true every day? Do other sections of the newspaper have the same ratio of pictures, statistics, and text as the sports section?

S-p-e-l-l-i-n-g

From the words used in newspaper headlines and accounts of your favorite sport, create a spelling list of ten words. Have a friend try to spell your words. Did your friend make any errors? Have your friend try his or her spelling list on you. Who made the fewest errors? Are there words that most of the class chose? Make a class list of those words.

© Dale Seymour Publications ®

A Picture's Worth

What's My Rule?

Collect sports pictures from the newspaper. With a friend, decide on a rule to sort the pictures into two piles. With your sorted pictures, approach two other classmates. Can they guess your reasoning for putting a picture in one pile rather than the other?

Words and Pictures

Below pictures in the newspaper are captions, or cutlines, as they say in the newspaper business. Collect action pictures and cutlines for your favorite sport. Cut off a cutline and give the remaining picture to a friend. Have your friend write a cutline for the picture. Compare your friend's cutline to the newspaper's. Have your friend choose a different picture. This time you create the cutline. Do you think writing cutlines is an easy job?

Picture Perfect

For several days, cut out pictures from the sports section of the newspaper. Estimate their size and place them in order from smallest to largest. Measure the length and width of each picture and record your results. Find the perimeter and area of each picture. Record these results. What is the best method to compare the size of pictures: length, width, perimeter, or area? Explain your reasoning in a short paragraph.

Pics and Cuts

From the newspaper, collect pictures and cutlines from your favorite sport. Cut off the cutlines and spread the pictures out in front of a friend. Read a cutline out loud and ask your friend to find the matching picture. Continue until all the pictures and cutlines have been matched.

The Medium Is the Message

Banner Day

Create a banner to cheer on your favorite team. What would make an exciting banner? In small groups, brainstorm for ideas. Share these ideas with the whole class. Having heard other's ideas, decide on the key elements of your group's banner. Do a rough sketch of your banner on big sheets of blank paper. If possible, create your banner on an old bedsheet. For best results, add color with paint or chalk. Present your banner to the class. As a class, decide which of the banners would be most effective on TV. Why?

The One-Minute Broadcaster

Suppose you are a radio announcer for your favorite sport. You have been assigned a one-minute time slot to report on that sport. In a small group, using the newspaper as a source, brainstorm for ideas for the script. Write a one-minute script. Present your radio broadcast to the class.

Sports Rap

Are you into rap music? Form a rap group with other students; decide on a name for your rap group. Write a rap song for your favorite team. Involve as many of the players as possible. Look for their names in the newspaper. Perform your hit for the class.

Bulletin Board

Using pictures, captions, stories, and headlines from the newspaper, create a classroom bulletin board based on your favorite team.

A Word to the Wise

Fill in the Blanks

Choose a story about your favorite sport from the newspaper. Blank out every fifth word. Have a friend try to fill in the missing words so that the story makes sense.

Try the same activity with a news or feature story or editorial from another section of the newspaper.

Unbelievable

Sportswriters are always searching for words to express the excitement of a game. Read a newspaper account of a recent game. Circle the words that create a sense of excitement for you. Make a list of these words, then create your own sentences that use these words.

Actions Speak Louder . . .

What is your favorite sport? There are words used in that sport that are difficult to define. It is easier to learn their meaning by seeing the words acted out. Form a small group and prepare a skit to act out some of these words for the class. Was the class able to guess what word you had in mind?

Alphabet Soup

What do you think are the five most used letters in newspaper sports stories—a, b, c, or another letter? Work in a small group. Cut a sports story into paragraphs. Give a different paragraph to each group member. Record how many *a*'s, *b*'s, *c*'s, and so on, are used in each paragraph. Combine the individual results to get a group result. Was your group result different from your individual result? Is this surprising? Was your group result different from other groups? Did you guess the top five letters correctly? Explore the most frequently used word with two letters, with three letters, with four letters including a double letter, or the most frequent first two letters in a four-letter word.

What's the Story?

A Mixed-up Story

In a newspaper, find the main story about a game played by your favorite team. Count how many paragraphs are in this story. Cut out each paragraph, and on the back label them 1, 2, and so on so that you can put them in the correct order. Shuffle the paragraphs, then give them to a friend. Without looking at the label, have your friend put the paragraphs in order so that the story makes sense.

Would it be possible to have a different order of the paragraphs and still have the story make sense?

What's Your Point?

In the newspaper, read a story about a recent game played by your favorite team. Make a list of the key points in the story. With your list, give an oral presentation to a small group in your class. Then have each member of the group read the original story in the newspaper. Do they agree that you touched on all the key points of the story during your presentation?

The Five *W*'s and How

In their stories, reporters try to answer the questions who, what, when, where, why, and how. Choose an interesting story about your favorite sport from the newspaper. Beside each paragraph, write which of the six questions the paragraph answers.

Sportswriter

Suppose you are a sportswriter covering your favorite team. Watch a game on TV or listen to it on the radio. Take notes as the game progresses. Write a story describing the game. Compare your story with one that appears in the newspaper.

Another approach is to have somebody in the class tape the game. Then watch or listen to the game in class and write a story based on the tape. Compare your story to the story in the newspaper.

Favorite Team

Class Favorite

Choose a team as your class favorite. Survey your class to find out who is the favorite player on that team. Express your survey results with a colorful graph or a newspaper story.

Name Dropping

Using the newspaper as a source, make a list of 10 players from your favorite team. On a 10-by-10 grid, fill in each player's last name. You may write the name up, down, backward, or diagonally. Use one square per letter. Fill the remaining squares with any letters chosen at random. Give your 100-letter grid to a friend. Ask your friend to find and circle the 10 names. How could you make this activity easier? more difficult?

The Star of the Game

In the newspaper, find the main story about a game involving your favorite team. After reading the story, make your choice of star of the game. Using facts from the story, write a paragraph to support your choice for the star of the game.

The Interview

Suppose you are a reporter assigned to cover your favorite team. Which player would you choose to interview? Create six questions that you would like to ask that player. Share these questions with a friend.

In the newspaper, look for a story based on an interview with a player. After reading the story, decide which questions the reporter asked the player. Write these questions down and share them with a friend.

Answers

....

Page 2   Scores and Puzzles

1. Tigers 10, Brewers 4
2. Phillies 8, Mets 3
3. Expos 9, Pirates 3
4. Braves 8, Rockies 3
5. White Sox 5, A's 2
6. Red Sox 9, Twins 2
7. Orioles 6, Yankees 5
8. Dodgers 10, Reds 3

Page 3   Games of the Week

1. 4 to 2
2. A, one run difference
3. B, one game in ten
4. zero days
5. Thursday—an average of 12 runs were scored each game or Friday—71 runs were scored.
6. Monday—an average of $6\frac{2}{3}$ runs were scored each game.

Page 5   Classic Games

Phillies	0	3	2	1	3	0	0	8	6—23
Cubs	1	10	0	14	0	1	0	0	x—26
Tigers	0	0	0	2	0	1	0	0	0—3
Red Sox	0	3	0	0	0	2	17	1	x—23

Game 1 is baseball's highest scoring game. In Game 2, the Red Sox scored a record 17 runs in one inning.

Page 7   Who Will Win?

The team that scored first, won game 1, 2, 3, 7, 11, 12, 13, 14, 16, 17, 19, 20, 22, and 23 or $\frac{14}{25}$ games.

Page 9   It's a Hit

1. Butler .800, DeShields .500, Piazza .667, Wallach .250, Rodriguez .500, Karros .000, Mondesi .500, Offerman .333, Astocio .000
2. six different batting averages
3. Butler 4
4. Butler .800
5. Offerman and Wallach or Offerman and Rodriguez or Wallach and Rodriguez or DeShields and Piazza or Mondesi and Piazza
6. DeShields and Rodriguez or Mondesi and Rodriguez
7. It is fairer to a player who has not played in as many games and hasn't had as many at bats and as a result hasn't had as many opportunities to get hits.
8. .406

Page 12   Pitching Performances

1. Martinez 4.50; Ontiveros 13.50; Rogers and Smiley 9.00, Nomo 0.00
2. Smiley
3. Ontiveros Yes: He averages more than one run per inning. The rest didn't.
4. A pitcher could pitch poorly and allow many runs, but his team scores lots of runs so that he wins the game. His era would be a better indicator of how he pitched.

Page 14   Who's in First

1. Chicago GB 5; Oakland GB $8\frac{1}{2}$
2. Toronto GB $1\frac{1}{2}$; Baltimore GB 5

Page 21   Football Title Page

Yes, because of all the tie games.

Page 22   Weekend Games

1. Browns 5, Seahawks 22
2. Giants 20, Redskins 6
3. Saints 17, Packers 19
4. Raiders 20, Chiefs 31
5. Buccaneers 21, 49ers 45
6. Cardinals 15, Cowboys 20

Page 23   High and Low

1. 17, 9, 36, 26, 33, 50, 35, 48, 57, 43, 3, 51, 23
2. Cowboys 37, Vikings 20
3. Jets 3, Redskins 0
4. $\frac{5}{13}$ = 38%
5. $\frac{3}{13}$ = 23%

Page 25   Comebacks

Game 1, 2, 7, 11; $\frac{4}{12}$ = 33%

Page 34   Last Night's Scores

1. Southern Cal, 99 points
2. Georgetown 51, points
3. Southern Cal/California, 180 point total
4. Seton Hall/Georgetown, 124 point total
5. Indiana 72, Illinois 69, 3-point difference
6. Virginia 81, North Carolina State 58, 23-point difference.

Page 36 Winning Margin

1–5 points . . . . 5 games
6–10 points . . . . 6 games
11–15 points . . . . 4 games
16–20 points . . . . 2 games
21–25 points . . . . 1 game
26 or more points . . . . . . 2 games

If we define small winning margin as a point difference of 5 or fewer, then the answer is "no" as this happened in only $\frac{5}{20}$ = 25% of the games.

However, if we define small winning margin as a point difference of 10 or fewer, then the answer is "yes" as this happened in $\frac{11}{20}$ = 55% of the games.

Page 38 Average Games

Total 448 . . . . Total 379
Average 75 . . . . Average 63
1. The average score was 75 to 63
2. The more realistic average would be the one based on six games. The more games considered, the more realistic the average score.

Page 41 What's the Score

Warriors 23	30	22	29—104
Suns. 29	23	26	32—110
Hornets 20	25	22	25—92
Hawks 27	26	21	26—100
Bulls 23	21	18	16—78
Nicks 24	18	26	19—87
Trail Blazers 25	29	28	28—110
Clippers. 24	21	34	26—105

Page 43 A High-Scoring Game

Pistons . . . . 38 . 36   34   37   14   12   15—186
Nuggets . . . 34 . 40   39   32   14   12   13—184

Headline Examples
Pistons Edge Nuggets, 186–184
Highest Score Ever, 186–184
Rocky Mountain High Score

Page 44 Quarter-by-Quarter Explorations

1. 12 games: Game 1, 3, 4, 6, 7, 8, 9, 10, 12, 14, 18, 19
2. 7 games: Game 2, 3, 8, 11, 16, 17, 19

Page 46 Hoops Heroes

1. 6 foul shots
2. 49 points
3. 52 points
4. 7 two-point baskets
5. 8 three-point baskets

Page 48 Playing the Percentages

1. field goals $\frac{11}{21}$ = 52%

2. foul shots $\frac{16}{17}$ = 94%

3. Rodman, Ellis, Robinson, Daniels

4. Rodman $\frac{4}{6}$ = 67%

5. Anderson $\frac{6}{7}$ = 100%

Page 55 Hockey

Oilers 12, Blackhawks 9

Page 56 Checkerboard Scores

1. 4–3
2. 9%
3. 26%
4. 1 goal, 39%
5. 7 goals, 23%

Page 58 Closing the Gap

Jagr 20, Bure 14, Leetch 26

Page 60 Puzzlers

San Jose 32, 27
Anaheim. 10, 22
Toronto. 7, 47
New Jersey 30, 17
Pittsburgh 30, 7
Florida 12, 4

Page 67

Prime-time wrestling winner is Bret Hart.

Page 68 Olympic Gold

1. Janet Evans
2. 8:25.52
3. 4.82 sec
4. Dalby and Splichalova .054 sec
5. Evans and Lewis

Page 70 Which Country Did the Best?

1. Katja Seizinger, 1 minute 35.93 sec, Germany
2. Some things to consider: Do you count skiers from each country? Do you average the times of skiers from each country? Do you give more points to a skier in a higher position? How many points? Do you consider the country's population?

Page 71 More Which Country Did the Best?

Ski jumping and discus throwing are decided by distance, not time.

Page 72 On Track

1. From first to eighth: Burrell, Drummond, Esmie, Anderson, Williams, Jefferson, Neal, Delice
2. Burrell
3. 10.27 sec
4. Esmie and Anderson
5. Anderson would tie Esmie; Williams, Jefferson, and Neal would be tied.
6. From first to eighth: Perec, Gaviria, Bryzgina, Richardson-Briscoe, Nazarova, Richards, Stevens, Smith
7. Kaiser was 0.2 seconds from qualifying.
8. Gold: Perec; Silver: Bryzgina; Bronze: Gaviria

Page 73 More on Track

The field events are the high jump, shot put, long jump, and javelin throw.

Page 74 Which is the Fastest Sport?

From fastest to slowest: skateboarding, luge, downhill skiing, cycling, speed skating, running backwards, snowshoeing, swimming

It depends on the speed limit.

No, because of the different distances involved.

Page 75 On the Run

1. 4 sec
2. 1 minute 48 sec
3. Men 1 minute 13 sec; Women 5 minutes 56 seconds
4. Kipngok and Hwang; Meyer and Peterkova
5. 13 mph.
6. From the 17th to the 21st mile it is uphill.

Page 76 Figure Skating Figures

1.

	Placement Points	Order of Finish
Kerrigan	2.5	2
Baiul	2.0	1
Bonaly	5.5	4
Lu	5.0	3
Szewczenko	8.5	6*
Witt	11.0	7
Sato	8.5	5*
Chouinard	13.0	9
Rechnio	16.5	10
Harding	12.0	8

*If skaters are tied in placement points, then the higher ranking goes to the better free skater.

2. Answers will vary. A possible answer is

	Tech. Ranking	Free Skating Ranking	Placement Points	Order of Finish
Kerrigan	1	2	2.5	2
Baiul	2	1	2.0	1
Bonaly	3	7	8.5	7
Lu	4	8	10.0	8
Szewczenko	5	6	8.5	6
Witt	6	5	8.0	4
Sato	7	9	12.5	9
Chouinard	8	10	14.0	10
Rechnio	9	4	8.5	5
Harding	10	3	8.0	3

Page 78 World Cup Soccer

1.

Country	W	L	T	GF	GA
Romania	2	1	0	5	5
Switzerland	1	1	1	5	4
USA	1	1	1	3	3
Columbia	1	2	0	4	5

2. Poland 5, Peru 1
Poland 0, Italy 0
Poland 0, Cameroon 0
Italy 1, Cameroon 1
Italy 1, Peru 1
Cameroon 0, Peru 0

3. England 3, Poland 0
England 0, Morocco 0
England 0, Portugal 1
Morocco 0, Poland 0
Morocco 3, Portugal 1
Poland 1, Portugal 0

Page 81 Some Different Sports

grape 328, egg 317, frisbee 197, rolling pin 175, brick 146